QUERENCIA
SPRING 2023

QUERENCIA

Querencia Press, LLC
Chicago Illinois

QUERENCIA PRESS

© Copyright 2023

ISBN

978 1 959118 50 3

www.querenciapress.com

First Published in 2023

Querencia Press, LLC
Chicago IL

Printed & Bound in the United States of America

CONTENTS

FICTION 131

NON-FICTION 181

ABOUT THE CONTRIBUTORS 215

POETRY

Tightening – Steve Denehan (he/him)

It arrives
unwanted
all teeth and shadow
tiny, tiny castanet claws
to push against your skin
from the inside
scaley coils to tighten
around your spine
to lattice your ribcage
to pull you tight
into yourself
so that
you appear
by degrees
to disappear

it arrives
unwanted
and no amount of symphonies or birdsong or laughter or cut grass
or good food or bad jokes or kind eyes or sherbet fountains or snail
trails or cat purrs or thunderstorms or Christmases or coffee or
trampoline jumping or writing or vapour trails or smiles across the
car park or childhood memories or snow angels or magic tricks or
singing or love or love or love

no amount of anything
can stop it

Bottled Messages & Skimmed Answers – Milie Galindo (she/her)

1) *Spin the Bottle*

By the Liffey's bed,

expats / strays / were brought together by a condensation-inducing breath of

happenstance.

Happenstance & a handful of cloves. Mistaken for clover.

Heineken-green luck serenaded them from neon lights

    as they clandestinely sipped at it   the two of them the only 2 players

    of a 3-persons spin-the-bottle game   fizzy on a molecular level

They roamed / strolled / climbed.

    tacking each other onto the city   pinning innuendos to antlers

staring down the glass bottle   down to the arch   shaking it like a snowglobe

Barmbrack season came with half of the neon gone.

    Not consumed / Gone / Running out.

    Yet glaring. Yet sirenning from the south side of O'Connell bridge.

Soon after, Grafton Street's lights chimed in, ringing the last sips.

    Ginger powder stung their eyes and nutmeg tied their gingerly purring

tongues

    all pent up hop & barley & Georgian stateliness & Darts in the night as they

indulged separately

Their pulverised cinnamon was wiped away with the cloves & the crumbs from

their last meal.

And, with the cymbal clink of broken glass, they parted,

by the Liffey and its untouched bed.

Still, they say the neon hasn't fizzled out.

2) *Autocomplete Foam-filled Phantoms & a Magic-8-Ball*

On Guinness nights—wry, warm, coy, calcified, phallic & straight up randy.
When the modalities of sleep are riding the hamster-wheel gram.
When the pelican's beak beats your beady brow.
When your sheets are caught in the froth of interloping street lights.
Focus on the shallow pool of memories/fantasies gathering on your right temple:

<fluttering eyelashes - kinetic webs & poetic stems - tut-mongering traffic lights &
aw-inducing crossings - itchy spaces - even-keeled reels in black & froth & pint -
inkless but baroque words - snacking on monogamous bread - cherry beads on
frothy dreams - trudging up perky hills - peeling the carats off the onion ring -
lipless sips taken through coy swirls - a jukebox of sitcom catchphrases - harping
on do ré mi fa sol la SI SI SI do - autocomplete foam-filled phantoms>

Floral prints were watered with that pool. Bare thrills & chills were washed in it.
And that's why insomnia now plays pool in your mind. With a magic-8-ball. And
sheds black feathers all over your bed.
You sit up and start flipping bottle caps. Heads: she loves me. Tails: she doesn't.
There's wool over your eyes. And it's not the sleeping kind.
Skim the top. Chug it with the wee small hours.

New Desolation Row: Shooting Characters in a Barrel – Milie Galindo
(she/her)

It's a malted March morning. Sheldon crosses despite the amber light.
He goes, **knock knock knock** on Penny's door.
A white tank top on a barrel-chested man fills the aperture.
It's Tony, with his chipped tooth and man-slaughtering hands.
Sheldon, baffled, balks at the sight of the grinning Italian bear.
Frightened out of his wits, Shelly mumbles clammy interrogations as he trots
away from the much amused wiseguy.
> High above the roofs of the swanky suburb, bloodied cotton balls merge into an
> hemorrhaging bale.
> Skies are wounded from New Jersey to Henan via Westphalia.

It's all sliding *bare-assed* down hill from here.
At least Alec Baldwin weighs less in crushed carrots.
Curators will soon pass down the wisdom of his impressions.
On a grimmer note, only a counter shot away, Gavroche plays fifa with one hand.
Cause **Kaboom** goes *Law & Order*. Spare the rod, spoil the club.
Napoléon has a one-track-mind, and we all know solidarity isn't his favourite
ditty.
> Paracetamol isn't enough to stop the fever, floods and fires.
> Oceans and seas foam at the mouth. *Want a mint, dear?*

Oily insomnia on balsamic nights.
Even a teabag trail doesn't lead to REM land.
In the lobby, a baked Phoebe performs *Smelly Cat* for a skittish Shelly.
Until he finally conks out.
With the morning comes neither sun nor chicken, but soap.
Loneliness loiters, even in packed masked streets.
Covid and Batman are tied in iterations.
> Yawns wind and unwind, buffeting the coiling paint.
> The forces of the Starry Night are spayed. Only Heavy Circles are left.

You know it's bleak when even Rory's ivy curls gather no moss.
Postcards are plucked from the wilderness, and potted.
We're tracing next week from the template of the week before last.
Penny is belting out Journey's greatest hits,
she doesn't hear Sheldon's purelled & gloved knocks.
When we see ourselves in the mirror, we either see
a dented smile
Or complacent blings.
Yes, Meadow did park,
but it's a barrel's snotty nose that peaks through the door.

***

Joker in the Deck – Milie Galindo (she/her)

The king of Spades is high on crystals.

*

He started out with a winning hand and a laurel wreath.

His crib effortlessly grew. Stunting growth itself.

Through life he bore the clank of his name as a bargaining chip on

his shoulder.

*

Now, his elbows bend with a clink.

Now, he's a silver fox with Sterling clubs and a crumpled ace of

hearts.

The Queen of Hearts reaches higher than glass.

*

She rose through the ranks. Moving sideways. The only way for her

to move upward.

Ideas bulging with testosterone splayed across her path. Some were even hurled at her. But she ducked, her flip in place, cause she's never been one to flip out.

Honed elbows tripped on her creative savvy. Hordes of limping knights have learnt not to underestimate her.

*

She's a Queen in a Knight's suit. Kings better keep up cause she'll turn them loose.

The Jack of Clubs has reached his stride

*

He was a smarmy square with a personality that came in bulk.
He was kettle-headed and entitled. Expecting the ladder to fold at his feet.
He floundered daily in foul mediocrity, grasping at plastic straws.
What he did know was; he was just tinfoil for the King of Spades.
He hauled his chipped ego across Manhattan.
Until he finally took a dip into the mainland.

*

He learnt to look to his full house for comfort, not the office.

The King of Hearts is no longer sitting astride the bottle.

*

He was a broken tumbler.

Secrets trickled down his Chevy mouth.

His life was fun. Like a loaded gun. He'd often loosen the cork, only to find out that trouble sputters.

He dragged his leaking baggage across the country.

Escaping the ravenous suitcase after him.

Tripping on a beat identity.

When, at last, he enridged himself, wrapped his arms around his shivering alter-ego,

and healed.

*

He drives on, on a road that will always feel rugged. If not jagged.
Clattering hearts in the backseat.

Hooking Up with Your High School Boyfriend in Your Thirties –
Amanda Brown (she/her)

Zero out of five stars. Would not recommend.
He'll just break your heart all over again
and leave you to pick up the pieces of all
his broken promises. But he'll sneak away
with a fragment and you won't notice.
Until it's too late. And you'll keep looking
for that missing bit, trying to fill the hole,
but you can't find it. So, you patch
the empty space with angry poetry
and sad songs and hope he comes back
around so you can finish repairing what he broke.

Sweetheart, I'm in Minneapolis – Amanda Brown (she/her)

I tried to pretend
he left no more
than a crack.
That I was still
mostly intact.

But he shattered
me with those four
words. And left me
to pick up the pieces.
I didn't let him see
how they made
my hands bleed.

Embrace, Egon Schiele (1917) – Abby McKee (she/her)

i. (honig):

she clings to him,
holding him unimaginably close—

demonstrating her love,
in all the ways she could never begin to articulate.
the supple fabric of a stray blanket that knows too much,
pressed along her spine.

he's an art piece, and she fears
she will never be ready to share him with the world.

gentle tracing, tender caresses,
and promises laced between words that they remain
too scared to confabulate.

eyes fluttered closed, infinitesimal osculations to fill the spaces
between,
a hand on his cheek, a nose nestled between the point,
where the collarbone meets neck—

she's not sure she remembers, what it had felt like
to love and be loved from both sides of the sun—
but she is lost in miles and miles of his skin, and she somehow can
finally breathe.

tell her this, love—
wenn kunst ist lang und das leben ist kurz,
dann was ist das?

ii. (vögeln)

bold strokes,
bright colors,
sharp movements.

until day turns into night.
and only they fill the space between.
until they wander across eons—

to find one another,
in the silence following.

iii. (gift):

he allows himself to be coddled,
nuzzling into her skin—
while jagged and protruding rocks
line his dorsal.

finding solace in the pieces of her,
that he will never begin to find within himself.

he's shattered glass, and he's watching her
try to piece him together like a mosaic.

harsh pants, bitter and bruising scratches along his spine—
he begs her to always see him like this.
to never see him as the poison that eats him alive.

their blood has mingled in the wreckage—
crimson blended with honey and beige,
he has ruined her.

not quite sure where his body ends,
and where her body begins.
he holds his breath—and he prays.

tell him this, angel—
if art is long and life is brief,
then what is this?

Cathedral: – Abby McKee (she/her)

the cathedral's on fire.

mahogany pews that i once knelt at,
the stories i once read
engulfed in golden flames.
deep wine and maroon spines crackle,
the whispers of floods and arcs burn.

and amongst it all,
i'm drowning.
in holy water.
in sins.

the clock has stopped ticking,
their father has fled—
white marble disintegrates
walls that held hymns reduced to ash

and the people are screaming.
there're prayers on their lips
but i'm up to my ears
in tears.
in guilt.
i'm drowning.

children circle the mulberry bush,
the one we met at after prayer,
the one where i once realized that maybe
just maybe

we shouldn't be conduits for
a god who's become the vain betrayal of our sins.
my existence shouldn't be a sin—

and these children promise things
that they don't quite yet understand.
hand in devoted hand,
manibus iunctis
no longer clasped

and somehow they never see the fire
they only see the cross
why aren't they looking?
why can't they see the people?
who else is drowning in this forty-day flood?

the flames are at my feet,
licking up against the hems of my clothing,
i'm at the alter,
but i am not theirs,
i'm not here nor there.

they're burning us at the stake
and all they see
is stained glass melting.

they're in the pews watching and waiting,
and i'm praying for a savior
who would hate them for twisting his beliefs,
because the Cathedral is on fire
and our priest is holding the match.
and children are crying at the stake.

who knew fire could be blessed?
who knew holy water could be volatile?
who knew that prayers could become curses
and power could be stolen from you?
who knew that the beliefs of others
could start a war inside of you?

I still can't talk about what happened – Naoimh Rogers (she/they)

Sticks and stones were never thrown,
but they were dragged to our shore
by the waves of your words, every word.
Every word spoken incited a burning pain.
every word spoken, felt like a bone broken
under the weight of a tsunami of my shame,
my hurt, your anger, your words.
I can write these things now
because I'm no longer tethered
by the anchor of your abuse
but I can't say it out loud.
Every time I try to, I am pulled back
by the undertow of your shouts,
your screams, your anguish,
the fear of being ruined at my hands,
as though I wasn't destroyed by yours.
As though this isn't the same seabed
you made and forced me to sink to.
I still can't talk about what happened.

A Slight Ache – Naoimh Rogers (she/they)

You put the jam jar on the countertop and left the lid off.
I told you it would attract wasps, you said it wouldn't.
I ushered them out with careful hands.

I took the honey out of the fridge and forgot to put the lid on,
you killed the bees that came in with yesterday's copy of The Times
and left their bodies on my pillowcase.

This poem is shaped like a cock – Naoimh Rogers (she/they)

```
The first dick I ever saw was Zac Ef
ron's. It was nothing more than a limp
lump of skin and muscle hanging off of
a man much         more beautiful than i
t was. The onl         y impact it had on m
  e is that I rem         ember it. The first di
  ck pic I receiv         ed was from a man
  at least twice m         y age. Which he m
  ight have known         had he thought to a
  sk. It was covered         in hair, sprouting i
  t from places I didn         't even know men
  had. I only opened t         he message beca
  use I didn't know wh         at it was. The fir
  st time I touched a dick,         I was surprised
  d at how soft it was for         something I wa
  s told was hard. I'm still         as surprised by
  it now.The first time I h         ad a dick in my m
  outh, I ended up with s         ick in my hands. T
  he first time I let a m         an fuck me, I bled
  through my favo         urite Hello Kitty p
  ants.The fir         st time I fucked
  a man         I took back wh
                 at was taken f
                 rom   me
```

32

Birthday Poem – Kelsey Landhuis (she/her)

I miss the view from South Street
of the bell tower on a gray afternoon
in November the Eastern white pines
holding the line against
a totally bleak landscape
sap sluggish but still circulating
enough to offer faint chlorophyll hope
or however that works I'll ask Adam
the next time they're in town
and try to remember this time
although more and more the only
memories that stick are the ones
where I'm standing alone at the end
of some Midwestern street
waiting for someone to say
start

Baraboo – Kelsey Landhuis (she/her)

for Christmas your mom got us tickets to
the most haunted house in Wisconsin
on the drive to Spring Green we came up
with backstories for the hawks perched
on posts from forgotten fences while
I counted on my fingers all your
various laughs

we arrived to find the garden
covered in burlap and the carousel
roped off for the season so instead
I read about the architect's dead nerves
how he would hold his finger to a flame
and claim to feel no pain when the back of my
hand brushed against your coat I understood
why someone would lie about that

holograms in the buttermilk – Amanda Bennett (she/her)

my girlfriend and i are the only two flies at this buttermilk gathering and again
i feel the change   i am brighter   peppier   wittier   it's all a part
of keeping things light   i didn't dare notice the difference before loving her
what was the point of otherwise when i was the only one   i was used to
laughing from my chest   smiling with no eyes   and posing as if
the room was a camera   i thought being unreal would keep me safe
nobody hurts a hologram   but then i found her and learned how good
blackness feels when it's intimate   when it multiplies   i want to laugh from my belly
because it is the source of all life   being black in quiet places with her
brought me back from the nowhere i was   what must change
to make room for living

black is a place we carry – Amanda Bennett (she/her)

black is a place we carry like the tiny polaroid lou took of us that i keep
in my wallet   sometimes i take it out and look to remind myself of a day
i felt close to everybody because i was safe with you   the picture took
so long to develop   for a while we were just faint strokes of memory
in a frame of white milk   we were there i knew underneath it all
but the pregnant gap between the moment and the memory it becomes is
a particular canal of agony   i know i'm black in all my memories
but who was i in the moment   i am so fond of that picture
of us because it is weightless   soothing   familiar   how much
of my face will i choose to carry in this life   just enough to know i'm home

This Heat is for Feeling – Amanda Bennett (she/her)

The day is violet by the time we get back to our nest in the trees in new hampshire after spending part of the day on an illegal dock at a lake so beautiful I wished nobody owned it. But on the lake there are boats and people floating and waiting for joy to arrive in the hot gaze of the sun. We're waiting too but don't want to admit it because we're supposed to be happy with what we have and in that moment I realize in my body that I have anxiety. It shouldn't be a revelation to anyone least of all me but I think until that exact second in space I couldn't let it into my conscious mind because that would mean recognizing all the ways in which my life is just one tight tunnel of anxiety, one big fear of falling into the hole I've made for myself that fits just my body and not one ounce more. I sit next to you and we dangle our feet in the water and I try to stay in my body for five minutes, that's all I can take but we do it together for the first time and it's kind of nice maybe we should do this more often, yeah?

rest is the part in the waterfall – Amanda Bennett (she/her)

through the part in the waterfall i saw my own face   for the first time
reflected back to me in the space between the water and the world i
wished for   after quitting my life three weeks ago   and coming inside
the warm wetness of the jungle in these blue mountains   the tangle of
memories that share my name are coming undone in my hands   like
shoelaces   like braids   like a fish's rainbow skin   when i hold these
scales in my hands i know that i was always worth the weight   i stayed
away from this place so long because i was afraid of being alone   but
to my surprise everybody came too   everybody i am followed in the
space of my footprints   in this land of rest i learned that we leave
footprints for those who share our faces on the inside   i want to learn
my inside faces   they come out against the rush of water like i did the
first time i was born   i am my mother's inside face   is that why she
could not see me   i know that now   i know that now   i know that now
away from everybody except my inside faces i baptize myself again and
again and again and again in these cool quick waters until a portal
opens up like a cervix effacing and i step through with my big grown
body like a baby and wail as loud as my first cry   there is no shame in
being born   who says it only has to happen once   i'll be born as many
times as i need to   not to get it right   but to feel the force of
remembering lives that were not mine   but flow through me as easily
as i once coursed through my mother's veins   when i am at rest i am a
nursemaid for the dead   giving self-sweet milk to spirits with fast-
drying throats   my breasts contain as much food as i let them   i give to
you only as much as I give to myself   where there is hunger there is
distance   where there is scarcity there is fear   i will not fear this
closeness of love   taste my breasts and know abundance   milk was my
first waterfall   my first mirror   my first feeling of love   my mother
rested enough to give me life   i will rest enough to give you life   and
you   and you   and you   and you   and me

Besides Kim Kardashian – Emily Manzer (she/her)

There aren't many women who could be
More than womb, eyelash, feather duster,
Starved into a dead woman's dress and
Worshipped at the altar of sex and wedding cakes.

I'm afraid the only roles left to play
Are no fun, are no good.
What am I made of that makes me
Happiest on my knees tying shoelaces?

I can't let you tie my shoelaces,
He said the night we met, and
I frowned up at him
Denied my happy submission.

My denomination is for fanatics
With gold in our teeth and nothing to lose,
Smiling at things we can't see–
What could he know about that?

I told him he was beautiful and
He repeated the words back to me,
Disciple to disciple,
Nothing false but all true, true
Zealots for this sect of symmetry.

She slept karaoke dreams beside us,
Her white hair fanned out and a strawberry
Mouth waiting to kiss him
For the next three months or so.

When everything was ruined
I wrote him a letter that said
Kiss me in a dream I won't remember. Really
Make your mark. I wear these thorns like a symbol,

I'm devoted, I'm yours truly, this is not the
End of days I was promised.

Swampland Blues – Emily Manzer (she/her)

i miss who i was in the swampland. i miss the loss or cure of a place you can't outrun. i think i can smile simple smiles until my face loses the city & fall back, time a stream or arrow or hand on my thigh, to that place where we drove up & down main street on August nights in John's lifted truck or any of the other boys who were like strange brothers to me, never interested in me beyond driving up & down, to 711 and the highway & back, chewing gum as they chewed tobacco. i'd take a hit & never feel high but the feeling was so delicious—you know how it is to be someone else for a moment or an hour before slipping back into normal life where i was good. but that life in fast cars always felt more real, just innocent enough to think those days weren't ticking. our lives crossing for years, forever, always so far from leaving. bored in abandoned buildings, bored in wind, young bodies jumping over bonfires. reborn in the passenger seat, 250km an hour on a mountain road & i couldn't die yet. naked in the glacier water i knew cold & nothing else. i wasn't scared back then, not like this. jumping off cliffs we would scream so loud & wake like gods in the river below, screaming & smiling & gorgeous god things.

sometimes i wonder what will happen when they die, my strange brothers. their bodies only ever those bodies to me, orange in the fire light, those halos of cigarette smoke. always driving or drinking or laughing like their fathers. i think maybe truly they will stay alive so perfectly in my head. cliff-diving & shopping with me for lacy thongs in a mall 2 hours away. *only buy it if you'll use it* he said, meaning one day i'd have to grow up. i bought them & that night we all slept peacefully side by side & nobody kissed. my strange brothers & i, we don't run from anything. i couldn't run from this. they are always alive in my head.

Imagine a California – Emily Manzer (she/her)

Imagine a California where it's my body
    in the beach, on the wave.
Imagine a California where
        it's my body on the shore.

So sweet at 25, I imagine
    how sweet you might have been.
All you had to do was ask, you say,
    and you open the window.

This time you dream of me
    and the seagulls cry
and I can't sleep.
      I can't sleep.
         All you had to do was ask.

Imagine a California where I drowned that day.
Imagine a California where I
    never left the beach.

           I never left the beach.

Milk Tea – Emily Manzer (she/her)

I'm needing something gorgeous lately,
Bare skin and Sunday music,
Running through the forest when it rains and
Eating butterfish with strangers and a ladybug
Lands on my fingertip,
Opens and closes its wings
Until I could cry. Until it feels nice, like
Gorgeous, bright as the Japanese Maple
Beating her heart bloody
Over ungrateful ponds where children play.
I know breaking something fragile
Would feel good, like
Gorgeous, like opal nail, lazy crucifix.
Pleasure to wash down my milk tea.
These escapes leak into
Bodies, voice notes, memoirs
And I buoy back
Into the shapes I know so well.

Humbly I ask for moments and fragrance;
Greedily I ask for loose-lipped tulips,
Dead at my door.

Skipping School – Ann Kammerer (she/her)

She was a girl I didn't know well,
quiet, Catholic,
someone I'd seen at mass
wedged between a dark dad
and crew-cut brothers,
wrapped in a turtleneck,
wool and tights,
a confirmation medal hung
around her neck.

"I need a ride," Carol whispered.
"I don't know who to ask."

We planned to meet Friday,
9 a.m.,
at my Ford Falcon
in the high school lot.
We'd skip classes.
She'd bring lunch.

"Could you wait?" she asked.
"While I'm there, I mean?"

"Of course," I said.

Carol took my hand.
Her eyes wet.
Her glasses smeared.

"I know you won't tell," she said.
"My mom. She would die."

That Friday we drove,
ignoring seatbelts
and smoking Salems.
She recited directions
from a crumbled note,
eating a donut and swilling Red Pop,
one hand resting on her belly.

We bounced on busted pavement
past party stores and chipped-paint houses,
spying a hand-letter road sign
that proclaimed: "Clinic. Next right."
Taking deep breaths we turned,
seeing the nurse
waiting and framed,
backlit in the archway
of a plate glass door.

"You can stay here," Carol said.
"Or come in."

I nodded.
A wisp of her hair
floated to the floor mat.
Tapping her round shoes,
she butted her cigarette,
her blush etched with tears
as she softly said:
"I hope you like PB&J, and Coke."

Three Years After – Ann Kammerer (she/her)

The mom of a guy I liked
ran a clinic,
three years post Roe v. Wade,
a place where girls like me
could get pills,
and condoms,
and freedom from parents
who'd rip us to remnants
like a stained, spoiled shirt.

We prevent the unwanted, Renee said,
taking my hand,
then Debbie's,
saying she helped, too,
when prevention didn't work.

Jerry could drive you, she said.
He does that
for girls who need us,
and for friends like you.

She dabbed Debbie's tears then,
her thin violet veins
arched like petals
on her smooth white hand.

I'll be there, I said.
With Debbie I mean.
That's good, Renee said,
her clear eyes blinking,
as I told her the dad,
the guy from Debbie's backseat tryst,
had taken another girl
to the cul-de-sac of stars.

Behind Me – Ann Kammerer (she/her)

I thought
I had moved passed it,
found a good place,
a clean place,
someplace
shaded by trees,
overlooking
a tiny backyard,
a few kids playing
next door,
cardinals nesting in pines.

I read at night,
long books,
short books,
watching sitcoms
or playing records,
laying on shag carpet,
my head between
the speakers
of a portable stereo,
closing my eyes
after two 40-ouncers
of beer.

Things seemed
behind me,
until it started
downstairs,

low at first,
a few thuds,
some thumps,
dull shouts
then shatters,
varnished with
wails and screams.

One night
a door slammed.
I looked out,
barely parting
my curtains,
seeing him
in the parking lot,
his arms above his head,
wielding something
dark and square,
quivering in a shirt
with cut-out sleeves.

"God damn you," he yelled.
"Fucking bitch."

He hurtled a small TV
onto the pavement,
standing over it,
his chest heaving,
his fists clenched.

"Do ya like that?" he yelled.
"Want more?"

He paced,
swinging his sinewed arms,
tapping his temples,
knotting his fingers
in his hair.
Halting,
he looked skyward,
his legs splayed,
a line of sweat
soaking the center
of his shirt.

"I love you," he howled.
"I love you,
I love you,
I love you."

He kicked the back door.
He pounded and
rattled the handle,
echoing 'I love you'
in a hoarse mantra.

"Get away," a woman shrieked.

He stopped
and tossed his head,
his jaw set,
then banged again.

"Got damn it," he yelled.
"Let me in."

He grew quiet.
He whispered
to the door.
A latch clicked,
then a hinge creaked.
He stepped in,
the shouts dimming,
the crying a fade.

The busted TV
was still there the next day,
glistening remains
of black plastic and glass
in a slant of afternoon sun.

I heard a knock
and looked through
the peephole.
A cop was there,
his face lean and chiseled.
I opened the door.

"Hello 'mam," he said.
"Officer Pierce.
From the Lansing Police."

He filled the door frame,
his legs locked and v'd,
his hands resting
on his holster and belt.

"I have a few questions," he said.

I nodded,
not asking what.

He told me
there was an incident.
Downstairs.
Last night.

"Do you recognize
this man?"

He held up a mug shot
of a guy with grayed skin
and mud-colored hair,
his mouth a thick line,
his eyes sockets.

I inched closer.

"We're looking for him," he said.
"Have you seen him?"

I stepped back,
remembering the guy,
his reddened face,
the stacked skinny muscles
on his furied arms,
the way he hollered
and stomped.

"Take your time," the cop said.

I looked again,
saying yes,
then no,
then yes,
trying to block
the pushes and shoves
and blistering 'I love yous'
from years ago
when someone
raged for me.

Acknowledgement: Anatomy – Sari Richards (they/them)

Eleven paces too close
to a daughter who birthed two daughters.
This body is mine in your saying,
"this must be yours"

How I stayed close to your daughter
As if to say, "thank you for this opportunity
to be more like you"

Swollen and bent silhouette,
sole-fleshed figure never knowing when
it had been touched. Craving
narrow recognition of another's

voice of a white guy named John something
Despite scientific findings,
voice of someone not in denial
urgency is not capable of meeting liberation.
We only, actually, watch as you rush by.

You are so wrong about this, it is difficult admitting
you are so right about everything else.
Regardless, modeling self-inflicting-harm
as refrains that have, actually, served me well.

An exercise in how far i could go [and have you meet me there] –
Sari Richards (they/them)

still, on our couch and closer
yet it must not have been so close, as you are still meeting me there

Ripped open a year ago and hands grab at my wet ribs
till my abdomen was again a spongy, damp puddle in perpetual
motion
styrofoam beams being pressed and stuck to the broke and split
bone

Your hands glide across the now sutured and scarred stomach
pressing those thin and cold limbs, pressing
till the styrofoam rubbed and squeaked against each other

and still we were not so close
but I stopped meeting you there

Days later and an elderly man
spending his time in doctor offices for impaired vision "I am losing
My sight because I cannot stop masturbating"

And again, I thought
I am not meeting you there

Crumpling as I beg
Please move a little further away
not you—you never were too close

each time a constant
relishing in my abdominal decay

Re-Association – Sari Richards (they/them)

I'll forget sometimes
I can start there
a body to look at
realize this is mine

debut number performed
This morning forgetting
by now forgot
think say this is important
doing this twice
exit exist none-the-less
less-than important

engineering calm
last Sunday morning
bloated, aching, thirst
widening eyes greeting,
sun welcome back dear Earth

mourning what more to say
direction fade aimless to dirt
whose limp limb finger now
taught pixilating before an
opened wound

glance scratch scar
slick outstretched whole
getting ribbed teeth caught
that dash of a line never not being mine

This is a story – Lucas Kurmis (he/him)

This is a story of a brick wall
Impenetrable
This is a story of broken mortar and pestle
This is not a story that ends well

> This is a story of a wisp of air
> Blowing softly from ear to ear
> This is a story of a single cell
> This is not a story that ends well

This is a story of a rusted nail

> This is a story of a mighty gale

This is a story of the belief in hell

> This is not a story that ends well

Nothing fallen, but then again, nothing gained
> Maybe we were only ever in each other's way
> Maybe I don't really have that much to say
Maybe it's time to stop believing in fate

You were a gateway drug
  You were the idea of love
    You were a two-handed-hug
      You are swollen gums
        You were the sweet treat that comes before a rot in the teeth
          You are the space between cavities

> You were a failed project
> You were encapsulated regret .
> You were cancelled tickets to Summerset
> You are the face of death .
> You were the trees' fall leaves
> You were mold in holes of rotten trees
> You are the space between cavities

Lucas isn't like us – Lucas Kurmis (he/him)

Something's off
I don't know what

Lucas isn't like us
He does drugs
He does too much
He told me he did _____ once
It's sort of fucked up
It sort of fucked him up

Lucas isn't like us
He's always lost in thought
He doesn't talk enough
He only really speaks in songs
He sometimes speaks in tongues
He yells at God
He thinks God is talking to him
In songs

Lucas doesn't like us
I don't think he does
I don't think he likes anyone
No. I think he could love

A bouncer at a bar once
Looked at Lucas
And said there's something wrong with him
And wouldn't let him in

Lucas isn't like us
His internal clock must be off
His sleep pattern is wrong
He sleeps too much
He doesn't sleep enough
Lucas said he died once
It's sort of fucked up
It sort of fucked him up
Or maybe more than once
Or maybe he's just lost
Or a part of him was turned off

A lifetime in 200 words or less – Kristina Percy (she/her)
—*after Matthew Owen Smith*

A quarter of your own (fifth if you're lucky), gone before it starts. At first, together, you will drive & fly & text across ten thousand miles but eventually one more is too many. You'll promise to stay friends, & for years you will both call this the worst month of your life. Later you'll honeymoon close to home just so you can return when you need to wash your feet in the same sea. Every few years you meet each other again, anew: new doctor, new homeowners, new parents, newly parentless. No one would suspect your modest family to be so crowded. You work more than you want to. Sleep less. One of you will want a third child (you can imagine how that discussion ends). For a decade, you survive. Still, every spring you take your first vacation again. It helps: for even the highest tide, a necessary slack. After your children empty your home, your many ghosts wander freely, stretching, hungry. Best to banish them to your beach & find another spot to renew your limping vows. As it always did, in this last quarter (third if you're lucky) what matters most is that you arrive.

Woman – Audrey Timmins (she/her/hers)

Femininity is a dead carcass,
The woman in the corner shadows of my mind,
The nightmusic of the space between days,
The struggle to contain and repress and hide,
The poppyseed lemon loaf icing,
The body with no skin,
The divine destruction of sweeping my rings
Into the trash by mistake while cleaning
And remembering them years later
In the leaky elevator's streaked mirror
Where her hollow eyes meet mine.

Femininity is an acceptance,
But not from the person I want,
Not from a mother's unfeeling text bubble,
Not from the silence of the unrequited email,
But from the weight of buying my own razors,
The sinking to the ocean floor,
The lessons I had to teach myself,
Of womanhood I tinkered together by chance,
Hoping that one day the pieces will be enough
To soak up the rivers I bled out in mourning
The end of a matriarch's war.

(April 18th, 2020) – **Luke Young** (he/him)

A few days ago
There was snow
A slow spring start—
By warm Saturday
A lawn mower stride
Beneath empty trees
Echoes against houses
Filled with quarantined citizens

Tease – **Luke Young** (he/him)

Spring teases the northern landscapes
Routine snow flurries and blustery days
Require fireplaces and thick socks
The sun comes out but so do the sweaters

Life in this northern land takes great patience

Crow Corpse – **Luke Young** (he/him)

I find myself checking in
On the corpse of a crow
Artfully dangling
From the lowest branch of a red pine
Adjacent to the diocese drive

Rejuvenation – Daniel Moreschi (he/him)

A shroud of crowded canopies impedes
The probing shimmers of a daybreak's gaze
From animating barred, deprived arrays
Of shrubs and saplings flanked by stranded seeds.

What was a sylvan idyll now grows dry,
And sparse in parts. An ancient boundary ails
Alongside rung-root routes; A pillar fails
In sync with understories left to die.

Once lofty layers tilt, a leafy screen
Is duly breached by incandescent streaks
Of sunlit lances falling from the peaks
To grace the gapes and greenage with a sheen...

A soil-stoked flash pervades the forest floor
And in its wake flow smoldering refrains
Of smoky helixes and crimson veins
That loom where sheltered embers pulse and pour.

An all-engulfing current swiftly sweeps
Decayed debris; a glade of graves that spurs
This surging, fervid force. It whirls and stirs
With homing heaves that skim the rims of steeps.

A wind-borne flurry mounts the mounds and smites
The trunks of lonesome sequoias, where it sets
And elevates with blazing pirouettes:
A coup that climbs the crowns and claims the heights.

As dens and havens wane, a spate of quakes
Reverberate: A flood of fauna braves
A baleful labyrinth of amber waves
Amid nigrescent clouds and singeing lakes.

The morrows slowly ease their tempered strife
When hazy frays abate. A stillness comes.
No shrieks or calls are heard, nor thudding thrums,
Nor morning songs, nor flights. No signs of life.

Within this ashen aftermath, the earth
Looks scorched, unshapely and devoid of dews.
But tasteless shades in place of vibrant hues
Belie a subtle cycle of rebirth.

A burst of verdant filaments ascends
From pitch-black barks, and luscious tufts abound
From buried buds on desecrated ground:
Their new beginnings forged from stricken ends.

Sorry I missed you – Kelly Cutchin (she/her/hers)

I hold myself hostage in a vinyl record, match-
box apartment. Inches alone,
snow on the patio. Barefoot like my mother,

knees knocking the backbeat. Body late
to surrender, I blow the question through
harmonica reeds: Am I brave

or married? Two fingers ring
of gin spill me past the sliding door
I bare shoulder shimmy shiver, call it

in case the neighbors see, hallelujah.
Clean the chorus with rest-
less hips hungry for olives picked

from mouths of strangers. Funny
where my mind goes on broken
legs, ankles bound by such a nice man.

The bridge is bare yearning,
too earnest. Under pressure
of lyrics like kelly

green and stop and please
stay, I snap.
Bake it in a casserole dish,

greedy lips dragging cast iron
hungry for nameless cufflinks caught

between teeth. To be new

land, unsettled, empty
left hand swiping right
on a buzzcut two towns over.

Porch rails turn keys, I play
the single life out under cover
of what if.

The phone calls me
back, husband speed dial wishing for his hot
dinner, stirring reminder of my thirteen years

as a brunette tourniquet slapped
on in a waiting room for relief, respite care
patchworked from the spaces between my father's fingers

and calls from home I never return.
I am kept
with blackstrap molasses shame,

his shattered monument
to the old college try. If there was
just a little wind, maybe I could

follow it, let it save me
some time. I pick up the third
time he calls. Sorry I missed you.

An Exercise in Self-Containment – Kelly Cutchin (she/her/hers)

Preparing for my mother's visit,
I hide the evidence
of my shameless living,
stiff-hand novelty refrigerator magnets
from road trip rest stops into a wine bag.
I replace candids of my overbite
smiling beside friends she'll never meet
with Olan Mills girlhood grins she'll recognize,
my young tongue tied deciphering hard palate hieroglyphs.
Broken spines of chapbooks turn, now face the false back
of the shelf. I bleed ballpoint pens of competing color,
cast their carcasses into her crown. I dye
my hair with Dove chocolates. Her favorite.
The space under my bed becomes a museum
of bold choices. I am a coward, sallow
stomach crawling back three generations.

I shred my passport, use the scraps as potting soil.
Cast tulips out of their vase, give her their water to drink.
Rinse my mouth out with my best perfume,
wallpaper the guilty continent of my body with her recipes
for corn pudding, buttermilk pie, good wife.
She sits in the only chair left.
I hang mirrors down the hallway, try sending her there
when she searches for her reflection in my pantry
and purse pockets, under my heirloom chin.
She can only see with her hands
covering my face. At the brittle ceremony
of dinner, she swallows a lamb whole. There is nothing
left of me, either.

A Lesson in Self-Expression – Kelly Cutchin (she/her/hers)

I wear the outfit.
Neon lime turtleneck with a crude-oil members only
jacket and high waisted bell bottoms, my belly
dripping over the waistband, and I just laugh.
Confetti plaid coat with a hood to hold my hair like
it's just resting there on display, an altar
to offer things because I have so many, see? So
many things! I have so much!
I am so much! Here I am on your sidewalk and in
your condo and in your better dreams being as big
as I am. A fucking marvel. I crack myself open like a
coconut and share whatever squishy wet splashes
out when I lop the top off, just holding it out there
to you like, "Here." Not "You want some?" Not "You
thirsty?" Just here. Here's my juice dripping down
the arms of every person who makes it out of bed
that day. And I make sure to save some for house
calls because
no one deserves to go thirsty. I insist on myself. I
am the DoorDash of bisexual swamp witches, all
ding dong here I am, delivering on a promise. I
appear and you cackle. I don't mean to make a big
thing about it, but me being anywhere is a big thing,
really, because look at me. Just look at me. It's
taken me so long to get here and I think my hair has
gotten shinier from all the flipping. You'd think I'd
be
so tired but I'm not sorry. I can't manage another
second of watercolor apologies for being in the

way, I'm so fluorescent it's absurd. I say I told you
so
to the mirror. I slap my ass cheeks and flash the
backup camera
on my neighbor's Subaru. I whip out a tit any time I
feel like it and everyone is relieved. Finally,
everyone says, finally and lets out a big sigh and
then gets busy adoring me. Even the ones who got
tired of waiting, they come back around because
you just can't look away from a woman on fire. All
the light. You know? Who ever could?

Parthenogenesis – Kelly Cutchin (she/her/hers)

All the New Mexico Whiptails are female.
Can you imagine?
All of your mother's alleles
just sat in your lap
like a plate of Sunday supper.

I want to halve
these helpings. I want
the plate to be divided
more clearly, a place for her
wounds and a place for my
own. I want to
want to lick the plate
clean.

Reaching – Marshall Bood (he/him)

out to my friend
in the dust...
he is in the hallway
waiting...
falling back into the dust...
spinning in my underwear...
the taxi driver says it's cold out

in Emergency I say I am
trying to get help in all the wrong places...
why are you saying that, scolds my friend

my plan wasn't death...
I just wanted to sort out
some things in my apartment

Numbers – Marshall Bood (he/him)

I tap numbers
but never phone
anyone

When I turn on the light switch
the toxic gas is released
I turn into someone else

I am planning to move
They are planning to take it
away from me
I will never move

He was murdered here—
in the red bathtub

I listen to all the songs
with murders in them...
the flicker in song number 9

Spirits Leaving – Marshall Bood (he/him)

Down to the grocery store...
aisles with eyes

Back to the ATM
another receipt
to prove I was there
at that time

Always someone standing
by the pay phone

Covering my bathroom mirror
with newspapers

Steam escapes the bathtub
into winter night—
spirits leaving

Eulogy on the Edge of a Forest After Midnight – Sara Doty (she/her)

Wine stains suck the moisture from my mouth, create a desert,
        mountains of sand are ridgebacks over my tongue, the bottles

mouth pressed against my lips billows briny warmth in the cold
        midnight, seeping heat from throat hollow to fingertip. You

wait beside me, eager for another sip, the slender neck
        of the bottle feels like the neck of a dead swan. I killed

the bottle almost empty, maybe three swigs left for you,
        I pour them in the grass.

The smoky autumn intensity brings hints of yet
        to frost in the air, traveling through time to get to me,

through ink and blue, a forest beseeching light. You say,
        what happened in the dream you had last night?

The wind does not need to know what it already
        abstracted from my bones, so like hospital walls. Last night

the wash of adrenalin was like a taste, pungent in my mouth
        as I struggled, my name, a screaming echo in your voice,

to get my rifle and my flak jacket. I stood in my hallway
        confused in the blue dark, my body felt scrambled,

like your body became, your brain a shiny thing.
        Out on my small terrace I stood, the cold air grounded

me, it lowed my heart rate. I looked down at the tree line-
        (the one where we now stand), thinking hospitals

are like birds, both of their bones are hollow.
You snap a twig, it pops like a wishbone, marrow

is neither disgusting nor satisfying, even though
talking to you is both. Wine burns crimson, my swig is

neat, my teeth look like blood has stained them in moonlight filtered
down through the leaves, you say it is too cold for Georgia this time

of year. Your eyes are the color of the sky reflected on swords,
I should have told you that, my mouth coated in red sacrament.

American Meadows – Sara Doty (she/her)

Look upon this great green place
with ever-song emerald gold,
rhapsody in tree leaf symphony
of doubt and glory and wasted sheen.
Taste the purple dye, where the larkspurs grow,
along this meadow in bended knee,
smell the freedom of wild rose hedge
This desired whimsy of free wet land of green,
for this is the meadow! Oh, these meadows!
American meadows, as far as the eye can see

are worth your hands and your legs,
worth a sound that blinds in one beat, one head
splintered in a kevlar as useful as a daisy crown,
these meadows are worth a boot
with a foot still inside,
an ankle visible ,
worth an ear gently attached to a scalp,
an eye lid, a finger, a lone testicle in the dirt.

Yes! All for the meadows, these meadows,
American meadows as far as the eye can see.
Take away the expense and only feel the soft
fuzz of sweet grass, rolling blanket of meadow—

America! America! Shed your disgrace on the!
And oh, the meadows! These meadows
American meadows as far as the eye can see.

(2) – M. Hutman (she/her)

in darkness we mourn the selected years we reigned on earth in
heart chambers choked by extra thick curtains that did not allow the
light in: our sorrows were burned on stakes and our moonlight
wings led us towards gathering vocal chords of lyricism

we are of blood and lust and all things fair and wise to our
coordinated longitude and latitude: our hungers fed our spirits,
beauty and decay made us have an illusionary full tummy

we thaw the frost from our noncompliant sleep induction as we
gather strength and widowhood: we jump off of the roof together
and our achilles springs us towards our trembling promises

in the darkness the sun perished and how sublime the kindling of
our envious wandering fitted us in a union only we could ever
fathom: the jaundiced gods couldn't even create us

Spring Cleaning – Jess Gregory (she/her)

Growth. Change.
Fresh sheets, Light doonas.
Soft, pastel colours,
And ducklings, taking their first swim.

Flowers blooming,
Blasting,
Their toxic spores
Up my nose.

Chased out by hot, salty water,
With a side of visceral, green gunk.

Sunshine piercing,
Burning,
Threatening,
To mutate precious cells
Into something unspeakable.

Blood-soaked cloths
From the oozing sores
On hands and ankles
As I crawl, dripping, aching.

Scrubbing and scrubbing,
And scrubbing,
This ancient wood—
No longer alive
But still able to bear
The marks of your abuse.

The Lily – Jess Gregory (she/her)

Some say that the Lily is a flower
of grief; a gift that sheaths our guilt and shame.
Performative empathy, emerging
From a wreath, that's soon tossed and forgotten.
Yet to me, the Lily is a flower
Of peace. No milestone of death, but of the
Everchanging currents of life, and of
Seasons. For whom, death is both cyclical
And expected. No pure, white, unsullied peace,
but peace in the imperfect,
gritty, ruthless, and unjust nature of living.

Shrubs – Leonie Anderson (she/her)

Yesterday I drove past our old home
And I wept yet again. Shrubs had overtaken
The ground and a blanket of greenery smothered
The garden.

A place that once bloomed with fragrant jasmine
Freshness has become a cemetery of memories

I glanced at the granite stones we had vowed to
Paint brown, now they lay bare crouched beneath
The iron gate.

That was two decades ago, and glaciers of ice still
Abide in me, so now, every time I pass by—I melt
A little bit more each day

And somehow on the eve of our love
I find myself lingering, right here.

Changes – Leonie Anderson (she/her)

And even as the sun returns,
The rose petals shall bloom.
Spring will abate our worries
On tender cherry blossoms in June
Summer's skirt will hoist in the
Thickness of heatwaves.

The tumbling solitude of Octobers
Will paint pavements with orange hues

Genial November will come with her
Quietness to mend every aching heart

Frigid autumn will mourn, but soon
Daffodils will sing again. Winter's solace
Will lend her healing—and in glorious
January, we will savor hope
And begin again.

Liminitive Transition – Sam Indigo Lydia Sword Fern Parker
(they/theirs/she/hers)

In a moment for whom they could not have planned
Lovers or haters couple
The planets, the watchers watched in antiquity
Conspire and perspire
Outward swirls inward, and word enters our ward
You are conceived at the spear by the wayside
Congruent and prodirective
You carry the momentum of ancient rage, quelled by stimulation
And expected by time
You agree to remember before you go back
But I know you can't control the reflecting quality
In the moment for whom we could not have planned

FA – Sam Indigo Lydia Sword Fern Parker (they/theirs/she/hers)

Defiled song
Writ upon the wall
Fills its own lung
Force you to crawl for unheard commands
Silent song
Hewn into the wood
Yet to be sung
Misunderstood by an unrepentant man
Assumption of the fair-weather acolyte
Follows the trance of the spotlight
The one who bears the chisel hath spoke,
Though only the one who bears his time
Heard the rhyme
And the rest is disturbed
They clamor and perturb
For a piece of the word
A sliver of stone
Cut from the bone
The epitaph will never read right
For the souvenir of the fair-weather acolyte

I am a collection – Sam Indigo Lydia Sword Fern Parker
(they/theirs/she/hers)

Of all the things
Ever held in my pockets
Of mismatched change
And bygone lockets
Dampened palms
And secrets kept
A brass-toothed answer to
The sanctum where I wept

Beyond Infinity – Ixy (she/her)

They say, "the sky is the limit"
But I'd rather hear you say
"Take me to the moon
I *wanna be with the stars*
     Send me
           send me
               into orbit"

Light years past the horizon,
where hardly a telescope can see,
is the only place we can be
what we want
how we want.

Be the other half of my binary star
in a galaxy
     far,
          far away
gravitationally bound to me
so close that we appear as one.
We can streak through space
like a meteor or comet,
so bright that no nebula
or even black hole could stifle

*First published in *Contemporary Jo

Repellent – Ixy (she/her)

I'm the mosquito that buzzes in your ear
as soon as the earth has defrosted
by new warmth from the sun.
Nothing to give but discomfort
and a bright reminder that I was there
when all I wanted was my fill.

I spent my 25th birthday home
      alone.
I *had* plans
      until I didn't.
So I threw a pity party instead because
no one wanted to do anything with me.
      Hardly anyone wants to do anything with me.

I keep looking for what I give other people:
      Love, energy, admiration
I'm asking for too much
I'm too much.
Why else would I get
      flaked on? ignored? even lied to?

I'm doing it wrong!
I swarm and cling
due to pure adoration, or whatever I'm missing, but
that's the last thing you want
because my affection stings to the point of anaphylaxis
      But at least it's on the list

I'm the problem
        the lowest common denominator
I miss when things were simplified.
back when I didn't wonder how you felt about me,
what I mean to you,
my place in your life,
until you swat me away,
which may be the closest we'll be.

surf over sunflower swells – Anastasia Helena Fenald (she/her)
   —For Katie

sometimes, when the sunflowers swell a sea,
I can hear ocean waves whisper through
their tall stalks. sometimes, I dive in the rows
of green, pretending the scattered seeds
are precious pearls shucked fresh from large
oysters. sometimes, I am lost in silky sunshine
and I pretend that my shadow is the only one
in the world. sometimes, if I close my eyes,
I am the only one in the world and I am a star
surrounded by an ocean of light, pure enough
to cleanse all my past hurt.

what embers tell their daughters – Anastasia Helena Fenald
(she/her)
    —For Chanda

you are a flame / gentle / caught on the dew
in the morning meadow / sizzling, steaming /
careful not to singe a blade of grass / won't blacken
nature's jade / but instead, provide warmth
like the sun / be the catalyst for photosynthesis /
provide nourishment / rotate the world around you /
have life be your dance partner / waltz in swirl /
waltz in fire / waltz in the cycle of beginnings
and ends / listen now / a deer jumps through
clovers hidden in the grass / and an old truck
drives down the dirt road / catches a big rock
in the tire / metal jumps as the deer does/
the cassette tape skips.

girl scout badge: survival – Anastasia Helena Fenald (she/her)

—For Lindsay

your luck has run out man / in flames / female praying mantis
eating the male hunger / hunting / i am hungry / you look so good /
forest on fire roasting spit / time to burn at the stake / i lit
the match / i am the flame / time to reclaim myself / run run run run
my man / run run run / trip over your limbs / scrape your knees / look
over your shoulder / like how i've looked over my shoulder /
a lifetime of fear / of loneliness / of isolation / of survival / i am
so hungry / i am starving for security / my children need to eat /
my children my children my children / we call this a hunting
expedition / another word for this is known as / field trip.

A Total Schenectady of the Heart. – Andrew Daugherty (he/him)

The wind once whispered 'Edna,' and that was close enough.
I was mildly mortified, but that's par for the course
when each candy heart is counted like a chicken egg assumed
to grow into something meatier than a rooster's tragic bluff.

My transparent invitations via pop songs shouted hoarse
summarized my status as an ill-tuxedoed groom
who seems like the best man if I stay standing long enough
and you get all of your news from a disreputable source.

So when the next step, like the Emperor's wardrobe, loomed
and you found it far too simple to just trip and fall in love,
you tattle-told me tall tales about the gift and the curse
of finding what you found far too close up in your zoom.

You can find good lumber cheap but you may find the splitting rough,
and with all that work to come you'll see that your real threat is thirst.
And since every single ounce of spit I swap or spill is doomed,
I might have been your brand had you a taste for the cheap stuff.

I speak all seven of your languages and one of them is Morse;
I can beep-beep-beep goodbyes as quick as I va-va'd your vooms.
But I won't get bent out of shape or twist my pretzel into puffs
when I still have the chance to chew some chaw as a recourse.

I won't write any sob stories or keep skeletons entombed,
and don't take my words as gospel when they're little more than guff.
I don't doubt you for a second when you say you love all sorts
but you must aim a little higher if you hope to shoot the moon.

Flowers – Luis Lopez-Maldonado (he/him/they/them)
—*after Harold Zisla's Flowers - Polymer, 1979*

Mexican daisies open like doors. Pink carnations. Yellow sunflowers. White dahlias. *Flores* burning bursting bleeding bathing, in gold. Sadness dripping like paint. Aged mahogany sanded and carved curves spreading like thunder. Bang!

The *piñata* tares open

        candies spill from heaven

                Purple tulips.   Blue violets.

    Orange marigolds.

           Orchids screaming like murdered children.

Bang!   *Mas flores...*

Run-On-Sentence – Luis Lopez-Maldonado (he/him/they/them)

Okay maybe it's all about sex with *mí* all the time ofcourse I mean gay *sexo* man-pussies pounded raw bareback & unafraid, or maybe I just don't know how to be normal I mean what is normal right or what is art or what is a good poem I'm sure you don't know either & that's the *problema* with all this, the struggle for equality the survival mode us colored people have to be in 24/7 the way un-smart mothers tell their kids to look away at queer brown boys like *mí*, but really all I care about is a good bowl of *frijoles* with homemade *tortillas* maybe some ketchup or mac'n'cheese on the side & the thought of staying young forever after this world around us, maybe its all about the little black books hidden below the beds of holy men the little black books I saw after fucking a couple of priests at Notre Dame those little black books of naked men or boys smiling into cameras with their limp penises at first but as soon as you turn the page they become erect on the page stiff like the necks of Mexican roosters & they tell you not to tell anyone that it's a secret between me & you & I keep the secret for two years & fuck them once in a while but now all I do I jack-off to their memory, see I told you it was all about sex with *mí* but what can I say the head can't help what this queer xicanx body wants but maybe all I need is a kick in the ass and a big   thick juicy   throbbing

                                                        hug.

93

Glue Me Up – Luis Lopez-Maldonado (he/him/they/them)

up these broken wings with similes and metaphors
little stories of little gay boys and girls slapped on face
for wearing or hiding lace, little stories of twisted rivers,
dark rooms, foggy mirrors, bloody floors, because
gender-reveal parties should uncover glasses of water
lipstick should transform me into kitten cub lion
because these broken broken wings will fly again
and light will devour darkness and mice will swallow
elephant and simile will become reality, glue
cementing lungs to ribs to heart to soul.

Post-Trauma – Luis Lopez-Maldonado (he/him/they/them)

Everyday I pray that God kills you
that your body disappears
at night with no trace of your perfume
the faint smell of shampoo on your hair
no clothing items to be found
no evidence of your expiration

I keep myself human by crying
lamenting on things not worth a cent
times when you spoke to me in dead languages
and cursed at me in Hebrew
I knew, your brother told me

Still, I was angry when you blew me
after my father's funeral
didn't even finish me off
didn't even ask if I was okay
but who gives a fuck about me
throw me on the bed slap my ass
ram yourself inside me, you're welcome

Because this wounded poem also reminds me
of you of the countless internet hook-ups
you had when we were dating—
lies tattooed in my heart
dead Mexican lilies
songs of a-thousand crying *Lloronas*
what, you didn't think I would find out?

Last night on Cragislist.com
under personals/orange county/M4M
a man asked if I could bruise him gently
enter him from behind for the first time
age 43/married/VGL
and I told him yes
that's how we met, remember?
I was seventeen
I was young dumb
and in need of cum

But now all I have left of you
is in the garage
tape holds all I knew
sealed boxes from the post office
stacked in the corner
like abandoned Legos
like half-smashed dead bodies
in Juarez, Mexico
I took you there
for your birthday, remember?
and prayers spill like salt
my lips stay open but God
is nowhere to be found
and you are long gone
but not but gone gone
like racism like the kkk
like straights fucking gays.

Brown Lawns, OC Califas – Luis Lopez-Maldonado
(he/him/they/them)

Attn: White People
Blacks don't stink of B.O.
Indians don't reek of curry
Asians don't use too much garlic
Mexicans don't just cook and clean
And I have to agree.
And I have to concur.
And I have to hone in eyes wide
And re-teach your kids our history
And not whiten every hero
And detox the hate you instilled
Attn: OC people
Acceptance is the first step
Plastic does not equal perfection
Hipster eateries deserve no Michelins
Because my favorite part is driving
The 91 and smelling the faint perfume
Of cow shit and brushfire and smog.

Rivercide – Zoe Copeland (they/them)

Nitrates running off land into streams
Toxic waters killing fish
Dead bodies floating, becoming stagnant
Algal bloom
What's left alive suffocating inside the water
All dies slowly
Those that ought to feed on the dying
Start to dwindle
Ecosystem degradation in progress
Activism. Save our rivers!
Suits discuss. Targets too ambitious, cost too much
Let discharge slide
Cut back on inspection, low prosecution
Boost the economy
Livestock farms creating nitrate run off...

A Reckoning – Olivia Snowdrop (she/they)

sin has splashed my neck red since i was small and i always
knew i was the killer. scraping the plates after dinner on a
sunday, the jelly dessert, the crumble. the mumbling excuses
to exit fast and quiet, then race riotous up the carpeted stairs
where the beheadings began. it started like a plan, as though
someone wrote a script: each time our voices dipped low so
the adults wouldn't slow the merriment downstairs and hear
the crunch of child's bones. my first murder was a moan:
a cry into the night, and scrambling hands to fix, to placate.
to save face i was made baby, i was made tiny mute:

cuteness masks cruelty well, and age.

technology came, and new ways to prolong the suffering.
my mother wondering at the closed door, a question pressed
into her lips, and my benediction, knees on the bed. i bled
out the worst of it, or so i thought, in lines that dart under my
eyelids, sometimes still, when i struggle to sleep. the secret
didn't keep and i spilled ink on my family. i ruined the sheets
of the safe house and confessed to confusion. a blooming
contusion on the tapestry of our girlhood. i couldn't stay shut;
i'm sorry i stuttered but ultimately spout. the truth forced out.
i did my time. now, it's yours.

Play House – Olivia Snowdrop (she/they)

rubber plant leaves, gloss-sheen,
fake proposal, personality change.
stamp shame on back of hands,
club night, girl with a smirk and a
knack for tattoos.

branded dish soap, bubble rainbow, pristine handwashing and a
smile like a toilet bowl, like a clean
sink, gums pink and glowing, like
a shrimp sweet.

kisses for dinner, sick-mouth,
snivelling bastard. regret like
an aftertaste, like a chaser. later,
shift swap, find a new one, let
them
    watch how you handle it.

always remember your enjoy-
ment of the game.

Teen Queen Tram Dream – Olivia Snowdrop (she/they)

i watch the metrolink light turn on
and think about nights in colder weather
when even december couldn't deter me
from wearing only a thin faux leather
coat. i would choke on cigarette smoke
just get it down you a few small puffs
it feels good in my hand—something
to do. i would chew on my cheek and
peel the label off a cider bottle, nervous
garbling, warbling whiny babe. the taste
of a party bitter on my lips. grimacing
with every swig: all i long for is a scape-
goat. moats between the normal people
and the wallflowers *you pick your side.*
hide in a bathroom hide in a beer garden
hide in the hardened shell you've been
presenting as real and pray someone
notices. hopeless at this. friends like a
revolving door like a train station—they
check in until the shots hit and i start on
about childhood *you've got tears in your*
eye. callow sighing and the weight of the
world, resting on shoulders now too sweaty
for a jacket.

Kayaks in Spring Heat – Olivia Snowdrop (she/they)

this weather reminds me of you.
hot may afternoons. sticky
rain and earth that springs
beneath my shoes.

i take to the river. live beside her
bed. my body going in is the
loudest crash. a deafening fantasy.
i long for arms. not my own.

remember the small mouse moan
escaping from my lips when you
touched me here and the cheers
of a passing boat. nervous

laughter. if i dive in
will i float? will i find us?
we're bound to linear time.
you can't go back. so we

plough forward. to new things
new things new things new things
new things new things new things
new things new things new th—

I Am – Liz Yew (she/they)

Huewwwww. Huewwww. Huewww. I move as though it is my last day on earth. I am searching. My mother rumbles her momentary wisdom as she gathers her thoughts and swirls them around. She tries to convince me to stay. But I am distracted. Hueww. My father beckons from far below. Dry warm hands seeking my welcome. His soft breeze whispers in stillness "come and we'll be together". I am searching. Huew. For my sister, my blazing sister. Went and never came back.

the wreckage – Dani De Luca (she/her)

when the words *they found a mass* stain the air red, you convince yourself one life is enough, however short. you remember the wild green of seconds before your whole was reduced to parts. you remember your son telling you that same morning, *if i die, daddy's name dies too.* you remember places unseen, things undone, people unmet and unloved. you remember how you've finally grown electric, shocking yourself and those around you into rhythm. you remember how maybe *finally* is too late.

when the words *they found a mass* stain the air red, you pray to all the heavy hitters and to thistles and to hummingbirds, those with red throats and without. you promise to sink into deep affection with the sorrowed and sorrowful. you vow to stop procrastinating and allow time's trapped things to exhale. you remember the blank pages of unlived lives and watch yourself take crayon, marker, and pen to their blinding open, swearing to mark every last one.

when the words *they found a mass* stain the air red, you remember you won't always bleed this way. that you are just one of many needing the gift of gold. you remember your first kiss with dave salgado and how his fake tooth fell in your mouth. you remember your first horse named patches and your last named poet. you remember your father's soft hair and your best friend's bright eyes. you remember jack london saying *the most beautiful stories always start with wreckage.* then you hope. god, you hope. let *this* wreckage end beautifully.

Take(n) Back – Dani De Luca (she/her)

Since you will not,
I will save you,
Mother.

My 4t legs
upon your lap,
shaking.

I cry the un-
sayable things,
wipe your

hot tears from my
face. Hear Daddy
say, *you*

will be sick, just
like her. My sick?
Different.

My sick watches
as I slow save
myself.

After My Son Tells Me Mean People Are Just People Who Suffer Too Big – Dani De Luca (she/her)

I wonder if a wake of vultures
pays its respects before feeding.

The Blood of Our Trees – Dani De Luca (she/her)

My life was shaped before I was
Wasn't yours?

Before my skeleton hardened to bone
and myelin covered my nerves
my parents plotted the line
I'd achieve across

That line so very flat and thin—
like first ice in fallwinter—so easy
to break and crash through

Instead of wishing for another line,
I wished for another life, one in which
I could be Samantha or Elizabeth or Michelle.
Prettier names for prettier lives.

I wished for another life of altered runes
and twisted fates to wonder then wander
never arriving at the knotted branches
of my family's blood-let tree.

Because who they were, I am. And
who they weren't I am, too
(inescapable truth).

But maybe I need not wish
to be another with a fate
to wander and never arrive

Maybe I take a knot of branch (a spiky one)
And prick my finger, pressing 'til ruby forms
then smear it close to the roots of who I am
(and they are too) realizing my line was never

linear (they just taught it was). Every zig and zag
and back and forth, compressing my one and done's
and do again and again and again's to winter ice
10-layers deep.

I have no other life and am no other than my own line
unplotted (and better for it). I love across the stretched ice
strong and thick and drink from the blood of our trees,
their skeletons shaped before I was.

Fridge Magnets – Elaine Westnott-O'Brien (she/her)

On my fridge I want

A magnetic photograph of a
Chubby, happy cherub
That looks just like me.

A clumsy, joyful handprint
In primary colours
Held up by a Paw Patrol magnet

A grainy, grey blur of 12-week elation
Where I (and only I)
Can distinguish arms, legs, a cheeky smile.

On my fridge I have

An appointment card
For a fertility clinic
The fifth visit this year.

A calendar
Of ovulation
Menstruation
Eventually to include
Injections
Pessaries
More menstruation.

Magnets from
Paris, Dubai, The Bahamas,
New York City, baby.

But none from
Disneyland, Trabolgan, Legoland.

In my body I need

A fresh start
Not fresh blood

On the delicate skin of my abdomen I crave

Shiny victorious stretch marks
Not hurtful ugly bruises

A magnet needs
Both positive and negative
To hold on.

I hold on.

Interrogations on Sunday Morning – Bruce Robinson (he/him)

Today's paper, offshore in the driveway
awaiting its sustenance, its subsequent
demolishment, a heaving between

the fires and the columns, those antic
unlives neither there nor time to awaken,
the paper gives me meals, I'll let you know

how that ripeness feels, the tangerines
that woke you, avocados and peccadilloes,
shopping carts in the afterlife,

the cameras gaze at a tourist in their aisles,
zealous pilgrim in want of just what I'm,
no, a minimum purchase on this finite

horizon before the real line dims,
the question seats itself at the register,
just what to pay for, what to steal.

It's The Sediment That Counts – Bruce Robinson (he/him)

Step away, it's not the car, it's one of them,
the car's running fine, almost all cylinders,
or maybe it needs a tune-up,

there's an offstage stumble that
ranges over the ground as if
the engine's the big deuce mac

that keeps all that primo muck
on its toes, on its toes and kind,
because a bog keeps a body safe,

I mean, it's a swamp, right? And a swamp
makes no distinction—death is life, vice
versa, just like the mode d'emploi says,

or old advice before it falters
into brick, or you, or me,
before we're fed to the fire.

Orion Shoots First – Jane Palmer (she/they)

We tried twice
to stay up all night
and watch the stars
take their nightly journey
faint across the suburban sky.

The first time
we lay on a blanket in a soccer field
in the middle of the night
arms barely touching
our parents unaware of our location

It was a clear night
warm for March
we named the constellations we knew
Orion, the hunter,
Cassiopeia, the punished,
the big dipper makes me think of soup

we named other constellations
after what we had for lunch
or the sears tower
or that guy in our math class

we giggled until we saw
a bright flashlight
and a police officer
telling us to go home

we were trespassing
no one is allowed in the park
after dark

so much for public land
and public skies

The next time
we opted for my backyard
when my parents were out of town
we picked a hot summer night
with no clouds and a new moon
I fell asleep as we named new constellations
I woke up at dawn
cold and covered in dew

as if I had become the clover and grass
that tickled my neck

You stayed awake
and told me what you saw
as we ate cereal in blue bowls
in my empty kitchen.

you told me
about Draco, the dragon serpent
and Pegasus, the horse with wings
teasing one another
dancing without touching
with Polaris in between

I asked about Orion
and you told me
the hunter was hiding
from Scorpius
and would be back in the winter

I thought about how
Orion traveled
across the sky
always ready to shoot
always keeping his distance
from the one who harmed him

That's how I felt back then
until I met you
Rigid. Vigilant. Upright.
Watching. Waiting.
Ready to shoot first.

I stayed in motion
Knowing that pausing meant
I could be prey

With you
I could be still
I could put my bow and arrow down

I could fall asleep next to you
despite insisting like a kid
that I could stay up
to watch the stars

And when I awoke
to the chatter of birds
in the early dawn
as the sky was turning pink
I knew I would be ok
underneath the night sky.

That Night at the Bar by the Sea – **Jane Palmer** (she/they)

The night we met
we laughed and
told stories like
old friends.

I had never seen
so many stars.

I wanted to spend
my last night
visiting Mexico
under them,
with you.

But you,
the reasonable one,
walked me back
to my hotel
at midnight.

I didn't want to go
to my hotel.

I didn't want to go
home.

We hugged to say goodbye and
wondered if we'd ever
see each other again.

I watched you walk away
into the dark.
And when I turned
I almost stepped
on a baby turtle,
lost and alone.

I picked her up,
she fit in my palm,
and walked her to the sea
as she squirmed
practicing her strokes
on my hand.

I placed her gently
on the water
as the waves
drenched my shoes
and she swam away
into the dark sea
confidently.

The Yard Sale – Jane Palmer (she/they)

My therapist and I
are looking at junk
and deciding what to keep
and what to toss.

I want to keep it all.
She wants to toss it all.

I find a tennis racquet
and my best friend
from third grade
appears with a smile.

My friend asks me if I still play
a game I never played.
Memories are unreliable.
Hers and mine.

I see a friend from college
who is looking at a lamp.
She tells me she needs
a bus schedule
so she can get home.

I leave to find it,
by reading the sign
down the street,
but then I can't
find my way back to her.

An hour and a half passes
and she's missed
six buses.

I keep walking
along the bus's route.
The next time I see a bus
I get on, hoping it will take me
to the last place I saw her
or to another place in our past
when there was less junk to sift through.

When I find my way back,
it's late, everyone is gone.
The yard sale has ended.

The junk is still there.

I pick up an antique mirror
and decide to keep it
because without the past
we are not here.

Lonely Together – Jane Palmer (she/they)

Look, a hawk!
you say
and I look up
to appreciate
the spread of its wide wings as it soars.

I don't tell you it is a turkey vulture.

I have learned that I care about
precision
more than most
more than you
I have learned I can enjoy beauty
without the need to be right.

I stay silent
and think about
the other things I want to say to you
but don't.

I look at you,
at us on this porch,
surrounded by silence
lonely while together.

As the sun sets,
the fireflies start to appear.

When it gets cold,
we go inside.

When we go to bed,
you dream of soaring
through cloudless skies.

I dream of unsaid words
falling out of my mouth
and onto the ground.

The words decay overnight
for a vulture's morning feast.

Instructions for Repairing the Broken – Jane Palmer (she/they)

When something you love breaks,
like a clock that was your grandmother's
or another heirloom,
you might want to fix it immediately.

You might want to find
all the scattered pieces and
the right tools
to put the parts back
where they belong, or
where you think they belong.

Sometimes,
when it's a loved one
that is broken,
he will need time
to sit amidst the chaos,
to take a deep breath,
count the pieces
over and over,
replace the worn out, unusable parts,
start to heal the wounds from the fall,

and you'll learn that
he'll eventually pick himself up,
without your help,
and he'll put the pieces back
where he likes them best.

Mussel – Christian Ward (he/him)

Every shell is dipped in night.
Place an ear against the ceramic
to eavesdrop on fox squabbles,
crows watching rubbish bags
left split open like unfinished
operations, brambles unfurling
their fruit. Humans, extras
with no dialogue. Open every
shell to reveal day—the glazed
pottery, a perfect sky. Of course,
there's the meat: An orange muscle
on a ready-made plate. Quiet,
contemplative. I threw up the sea
the first time I tried it. Didn't know
I was chewing its prayer.

Gifted – Christian Ward (he/him)

In some light, the tally marks
on my side room's wall
cast roses' slant shadows.
A gift from a previous occupant.
Other times—camouflaged,
they slip into the grime and dirt.
Another gift: claw marks,
almost dinosaur-like, on the wall.
Small, intent. Childlike.
I hear scratching in the walls
in those moments between sleep
and waking, when the moon bobs
like a float above the clouds
and the neighbourhood
has put a hand on its mouth.
In this time, my fingers
bend to count the days the visitor
has left and when its shadow
will become an adult again.

Shark at the shore – Jo Bahdo (they/them)

I could pretend to be a shark
—of the lake, the rivers and the bathtub—
before, I found comfort in shapeshifting
exploiting my nebulous anatomy
in the water I could

                                    hold my breath for longer
                                    crane, knight, split
                                    have a choice beyond my
                    flesh

until they tagged me as *a whale of a girl*
urged to slenderise and soften my surface
constrained from a body of water
bound to a geotic silhouette, I forgot that

                                    immersed, the female label
would sink

                                    supine, the sun would
refine my chest

                                    lulled, the waves would
embody my curves

my home is not at the shore

Sea Witch – Elyssa Tappero (she/her)

take my voice, sea witch
grant me fine legs in return
a worthwhile bargain
even if each step pains
me at least I'll be like the
rest

take my voice, sea witch
after all, what use are words?
brief, untouchable
yet flesh is warm and solid
bone and blood make us human

take my voice, sea witch
I just want to be normal
feel the things I should
I long to walk on the shore
but now longing's not enough

take my voice, sea witch
change the self I never chose
give me sensation
for I've given up on words
and now I'd give anything

A PALM TREE MOVED OVER THE HOUSE
on thanksgiving before the holiday/ a lovesong for Blatty – david diaz (he/him)

what if i saw me floating
in my bedroom through the front-facing window
        from across the street

           with my sodium-fattened gaze
           into a better lit & somehow better
           possessed version adapted
           out of dirty mirror seance with cracked lips
           eyes bright with terror and piety

i'd stand in a small bed of fake hydrangeas or ambrosia
the toes of my sneakers wet with yellow-brown mud
        not gawking but compelled by magnetic
director's cut more honest than i'd ever

would the small pain-
tightened wires
behind my teeth
finally make an honest man
        from me
        /out of all this?
           a cold leaf behind
           my [otherwise warm] neck
           pissing on my feet at the dinner party
           while my mother's houseguests play

john carpenter theme songs
to talk about women floating
in the woods behind the library

p a z u z u is probably a common imprint
on a legal pad's second and third page
- next to added and subtracted numbers
- something scratched out with a thousand angry circles
nearly tearing through the paper
- a list of things to apologize for first

likely   though
just a discarded son
or old friend with cold feet
anxiously scribbling sad faces
near piecemeal memoirs
a bone they never thought
would need picking between
open on a hardly used but damaged desk
— regret   the antidote for happiness
to chase the high of first loss

on the last day before leaving
for our own problems and dancing beds
there are two priests   since the test
of wit, stomach, & sense of humor
is usually a losing bet 1:2
when the many inside are only
one   panic sets

             since it shouldn't be so difficult
             to control, then

momentary shutter of a clock
resets the earth so it can bless
itself to heal like scar tissue
             lungs & heart & brain
             beneath a web of cheesecloth
                     regrown in paper
             like dirty gauze—   never good
                                        again & always
                                        making up for it

FICTION

ME FT. YOUR HAND – Hasrat Chawla (she/her)

PALM

The epicenter of warmth resides in the lines that have disconnected due to years of life. They're the incomplete beauty. I suffice when they touch my face. A lover blooms when a dash of sunlight is caught in the cups you make out of your palms. There is no other way to it—I am the lover. Often, I reside in a thought of someone looking at me gawking at you while crossing the road holding my hand; looking at the embodiment of confidence. Yesterday you asked me to remember your card number while my skin was stroking the epicenter; I said "right now, I can't remember who I am".

My waist, my cheeks, my name, my dreams, deserve your caress. I have been lost until I found your Atlas Palms.

FINGERTIPS

We were koi no yokan. We happened gradually. In between the space that our ripening brought, your fingertips delivered what was meant for me. They never asked for permission, kept re-visiting every inch of me that looked for you. I'm sure our cells first exchanged through the tips of our epidermis and we became each other. I'm sure the cells will keep exchanging. It's intense when you trace my lips. It's startling when the sky rips up to witness the beauty of the trace; the perfect passion it brings. Your fingertips are best at what they do with my skin. Your fingertips are like the spoons made up of delicacies exclusive to me, like the lovers made up of ocean with no instability, the fragments of a fist built to hurt me, they're everything that I've lost, everything that can ever be mine.

The wideness of each, calms my fear of not having enough space in this world for myself. Just 10 fingertips are enough.

BACK

Nothing doesn't suit you—short nails, chopped cuticles, showing nerves, strong humanness. My palm is the place the back of your hand was meant to fit it. I hold it and a world of unfitted beauty revolves around my eyes. The magic of unevenness, the rooted sobriety, the uplift of distinguished togetherness. It keeps on brushing mine when we walk together but far away mentally; it brings us back to each other. The back of your hand is a perfect shield to my entire life of insecurities and to our dance of insanity before the artless. I hate an obstacle between your voice and my ears and the back of your hand is sometimes that; can you please keep it elsewhere while you speak? The amount of valor mixed with appropriate softness one punch carries gives me the confidence to let my head rest on you for the rest of my life.

Look, I know it's not the right time, but whenever it'll be, I'll grace the back of your hand with a square-shaped gold ring because my love isn't a circle with no end, it's a square with edges a little too mismatched at times, but a ring in any shape never ends, does it ?

WRIST

First—I want to be your soldered bracelet. Second—to have the best grip, I hold you from the place of your life veins, your wrist. The grip steadily transforms into a realisation of reality with you; a reality where wristwatches are a waste because we make each other timeless.

I fondle you exactly where blood runs in. And I eavesdrop on your soft moans. Your unsaid desire to never stop it pushes me to like wrists a little more for their romantic functionality. I wait for the moment you hold my wrist to slip in your hand in mine because that's where it brings from and that's the place which stops time.

Nanang – Cathleen Balid (she/her)

is a word that has always sat funny in your mouth. You say it with the back of your tongue, your teeth stale and pristine, and you note the breath in its odd timedness, smooth and circular like nanang's rosary beads. Maybe that is why you say it like a prayer: eyes closed, lips waxy. Breathing measured like your body.

Nanang is a word that means mother, but you have never seen it before. Somehow the word only exists in the space between cost and silence, between nanang's antiseptic eyes, as in, *yes, nanang, I saw the bills.* As in, *no, nanang, I don't know what to do.* You only knew nanang through her thin, slippery body, the way her dreams slipped past her coffee-stained teeth and paused

into farming sugar. Through the absent way she said your name, like a stain of coffee knelt into a tablecloth, flattened by its bitterness. Over the years you watched nanang's back grow broken like webbed fruit rinds swallowed and discarded, and you palmed your spine faintly and imagined your bloody bone developed from hers—a skeletal connection. But nanang swallows affection as if it were bitter medicine, and you, embittered, swallow her name into the striated depths of your voice.

Nanang is a word that you have not said since you left her, dying, in the house you were born in. In time nanang would learn to clutch her words so they did not fracture, to amend them into a reflection of her body, but you did not stay for time. You lost your youth to mending the ripples across nanang's lonely, absent face, smoothing a future serrated like the peel of durian, and

when you left, you brushed the wetness from her cheek. It has been years since you have seen nanang's filmy lips, touched her wrinkled skin, but

nanang is a word that falls reflexive from your mouth.

Ghosts. – Janna Lopez (she/her)

I've been dead a day. Or maybe a week. Or thereabouts. Dead time's hard to gauge. I'm new at being dead. I'm immeasurably sad that I'm dead; a sadness that hurts and leaks and aches sorrow. A sensation to touch earth overwhelms. Even if the earth's air, it's very breath, is despondent.

In death, I'm unsure whose sadness wins: my own, or grief from those alive. It's selfish to absorb my own passing, but it was my only life. When it's your one life, it stands to reason it's your one death. Who wants to take on the belonging of someone else's sadness? No one wants to wear someone else's goodbye.

I cannot clearly see earth. I am above and below. I am upside down, thrust against lines, rigid grids that clash with the earth's curve, in disharmony with curling waves only aliveness rolls forward.

I'm on the outside, unable to discern definitive shadows of trees and concrete and windows and rooftops and flying birds. They are gray; shapeless. They are uniform, void of outline. Through death my sunken eyes only see waves of gray, of light, ripples of matter that exist, but no longer exist in a form I can see.

I cannot be seen. I'm dead long enough—I'm not yet a ghost. Will the seeing of my deadness, by anyone who loved me, the acknowledgement I'm gone, the acceptance of my departure, make me the ghost? How long will hearts of those who loved me own that I'm gone? Do pieces of my ghost appear more brightly, as darkness of acceptance seeps in?

How many of my passing ghosts must I see, before the outline of my own becomes visible? Where do my ghosts begin?

Since my beginning—the sudden explosion of light and cold, a tenuous second allowing the womb that was, and a world to be, to coalesce; ghosts of rapidly-moving wind filling tiny lungs to force breath. The shriek of being alive. The first eternal gaze into my mother's hopeful eyes. The steady comfort of my grandmother's arms as she cradled a me that was bundled beneath a clean-smelling blanket. Hearts full, beaming from encircled family and friends, an orb above us, glowing from unquestioned hope birthed from new life. My new life. The circle held hope mine would be a good life. A full life. A long life.

I was truly loved then, wasn't I?

Isn't this the kind of love that new life impresses upon us, to drip and drift far beneath our tiny newborn bones, to reach our cells, and our spirit, to carry us through a life of doubt and pain? Did I feel that encircled hopeful love in my death? Did it make it to my end as once promised?

Beyond birth, carrying the burden from buried childhood ghosts, trying to die free.

Ghosts of tears left in a crib—my mother walking away, door shut behind her to drown out my cries, as tiny legs kicked in the dark. Unrealized hope for a return—*please don't leave*—crying until no tears were left. These tears have big ghosts because they never fully died. They never left and wandered my heart. Maybe the death tears I now cry hold my childhood's sadness of being alone.

Ghosts left wondering where the hopeful
love went that once encircled me. Ghosts
of frilly dresses soiled by missed mouthfuls
of spoon-fed peas.

Ghosts of skinned knees and pink Huffy bikes and Candyland and
Easy Bake ovens and Fashion Barbie heads and watching cartoons
after school and walks to McDonald's for cheeseburger happy
meals and fights with my brother over cereal box toys and secret
clubs with neighborhood kids and ghosts of lost loves, and teachers
who believed in me, and ghosts of cafeteria lunches of sloppy joes,
and big elementary school hallways when I felt so small, and
certainty when my mom was unable, my grandparents always
loved me, their circle of love continued, endured, after being left on
my own, to fend on my own—tears from these ghosts never left
me.

In my death, are these the tears I carry, and must release, before
my ghosts are free?

In death I only hear voices of regret. The ones which can recall that
ancient love, remain silent. I wish death was silent. I hear every
voice I disappointed. Every echo of unspoken words. Every apology
I couldn't utter. Every dream I left ignored. These are a cacophony
of unheard sounds that beg for release upon death, to be free from
trapped silence that stored them. My dead body's ears no longer
hold my head. They float away, and back, and away again, attached
by the line of a stretched lone drum. An elastic tether of
recollection, music, anger, sadness, wind, waves, busyness, details,
and dreams. They heard what the heart whispered as real and true,
if only for a moment. Death ears listen to the fibers of
everythingness, of belonging and sorrow. The sounds life makes

when even you can't hear them. Ghosts of all I couldn't hear, tell me so in death.

I'm sad for all I couldn't hear. And sadder for all I could.

The time I've been dead I wonder who cries? Whose heart stalls from my passing? Who will carry forward my name, my face, the sound of my voice? I'll be a known ghost for a generation maybe two, only to become an unknown ghost, an infinite ghost, once the last person to know me dies. Would I want to be a ghost forever? Shouldn't ghosts die too? How does one die a death once they're already dead? What does that sound like? Maybe a ghost death is truly silent.

In this death I hear windchimes and pounding hammers and fast-moving trucks and buzzing bees and squawking ducks and echoes of regret. Voices carry regret and through echoes I stretch to hear one more time the chorus of my estranged daughter's voice. Her voice's texture was an embedded wandering ghost before I died. Yet, I want to tattoo the memory. The imprint of her soft hand, childhood fingertips with perpetually bitten nails, the ones that once welcomed me, as she sought the shelter of her hand in mine. The tenderness of her hand is alive.

For many days I carried Alayna's voice in a hollow heart that echoed her familiar laugh. The echo was deep with regret and pain that somewhere we'd died although she was still, always, and infinitely, very much alive in me. For her, We died. Now that I'm dead, will We die with me? What of me will Alayna carry throughout her life as her own ghosts of tears and regret? Without our voices reaching each other's, will her petrified ghosts of anger ever be silenced?

***

A month or day or week before I died, I dreamt I wept at the river. A premonition of my death was alive. What I saw and felt deep within, was as if death wanted to ease into me. I stood on a wooded bluff and softly cried while watching the sun sparkle off moving water below. The wavy surface flashed like glitter. The sky was cloudless and painted bright blue. Delicate leaves from surrounding birch trees flittered in the breeze. In the distance, going upriver, against the wind, was a silver boat. I couldn't see much, it was far, but I could see that no one was in front steering it. The silver boat glided against the current in slow motion. When it finally reached the bluff, far below, there was a hooded figure sitting at the back of the boat. I couldn't make out a face or eyes or humanly shape but I felt it—as the boat crawled passed—the hooded figure was death, and from 100 yards away, I could feel it peering darkness into me. All motion came to a halt— the flittering leaves, the rushing wind, the sparkling river—as the slow boat churned by...

***

Now that I'm dead the single pain of my life is clear: I wanted to belong. My life became a restless search. All I wanted, and didn't know how to name what I wanted, was to inhabit a bodily integration of *belonging*. A belonging—attached and wanted—when trust, faith, and certainty, of love without provision, were so clear, my tired heart could rest.

My innocence never gave up. I searched and searched.

Words never matched my prayer to belong. I imagined a butterfly, in a garden, flittering above rows of prickly weeds, searching through a landscape of sharp edges, narrow thorns, hoping to glimpse one soft flower to land. One small beacon of bright silky petals. Tired, flying, flittering, moving, hovering, surveying below, no soft place to touch down, no pillows to make room for tired wings in need of rest. In my life, that's what belonging looked like. I was unable to land. In death, I can name it. Belonging was my heart's unfulfilled pain.

The Good Euf – D.M. Rice (they/them)

Maman knew the streets of Hong Kong were no place to bud, so she sought help from a higher power. Each day, carrying fifty kilos of lotus flower, hardly noticing her own smell for the char of incense. Upstairs, Pa runs the anteroom with all of the tact of a great bull. Some men you can only keep at home, or else nothing would ever get done. Li Po and Ang Fun have been passing the same tenner between them for almost forty years, their furrow of sweat and steam at the adrenaline, the rush of exposure. My grace at the curtain window.

Another health inspector who thinks they can get one better on them. Yes, that door was sealed at the time of purchase. No, there are no fire exits from the ground floor. Isn't the front door a fire exit? All of the patience of the ancestors for those who meddle in red tape. The squat, beetle-eyed man on the balcony, stooping to stare at the sign, written in flawless calligraphy:

NOW YOU MUSN'T JUMP!
RESPECT THE OWNERS
AND YOURSELF!

You're going to need an English translation publicly available, I'm afraid.
Yes. We will print and frame it.
Do you maintain a relationship with the previous owner?
He occasionally comes in as a customer. We don't give him a discount or anything, though.
How long have you resided at the premises?
Seven years to the date, sir.

Are those real jade statues?

That is real jade. Up there you can see real white marble.

Those framed rubies are fake.

Would you say it has been difficult refraining from delivery service with a restaurant of this caliber?

What do you mean? Other people can deliver if they want, but we have no part of it. We make no money from it, you've seen in our records.

Yes, well. I believe that is everything. Expect to receive the report for this review by the first of next month. Thank you for your time and patience through this routine matter of governance.

Thank you, Mr. Inspector. On behalf of my family, we would like to bestow this small token of appreciation to you.

Oh, really, that's not necessary.

Please, please. Don't insult us by opening it here. You must see hundreds of buildings and receive little in the way of gratitude. Now, thanks for your time. Please, please. If you ever need to come and visit again, we will welcome you with open arms.

Sarah running through the breakboards, the whimsy in her whisper.

She gave the man the money! He took the money!

How much do you think it was?

Not sure. Hundreds? Thousands? Depends on what bills they were.

How is Maman?

She looks calm, even relieved a bit. Smoking with Chan on the balcony.

Do you think he'll keep it?

If you had seen him yourself, you wouldn't even ask.

The dust of the room burst with each excitable step. Nails digging into the wood, hard gasps of exchange. When Maman catches them in the restaurant, she pretends like they're somebody else's—if a family friend is available, if not, into the street and out of the back entrance again, for a scold later. They learn to look after each other. Respect is fear.

He loved the plastic water lilies and ginkgo trees and bushes that buffered the empty spaces, hid the cracks in the wall. There was something of an authenticity to it that the townies here craved, like being transported to another dimension. So he would bring anyone and everyone that he could convince to walk in the door, promising the fruit of generations, time-honed delicacies, simplicity for substance. They eventually realized he was too scared to take the money elsewhere. Groups of eight of ten, checking the menus for caked remains, feeling their fingers on the underside of tables as they walked, always eying the corners for moving shadows. The dull numb conversation of regulatory praxis. Fluttering children hiding in the piety, on the far end of the bar. How many bottles of wine equaled suspicion? Variations on a theme. Cognitive formalisms based on fear and insecurity.

He is always here, Liu!
But his business brings more business, we musn't upset him.
   They will ask questions, they will see something. How are we
   going to keep our operation if we have a bunch of
   government heads prodding us with their stupid chatter?
No, no, Shui, the gameroom is running as smoothly as ever, and
they can't see past their drunken noses. We will comp a few
cocktails, and they'll never shove their curiosity where it doesn't
belong.

145

There in the fields of the chat-o was the only freedom. Brushes of lavender, endless burrows of rabbits and foxes. Little Ryan crying over the broken rattle-drum, unable to cope with the torn skin. Strange words in the villa. The suited men with wide-brimmed hats, heavy breath like liquorice smoke. Talk about the middle passage, changelings for merchandise. Languages made to forbid. Languages to invite. But the others around couldn't understand any of them. They couldn't understand any of the others. Driver Mike and the rest never walked through the front door but knew something was going on. They cut their chatter short and made no kindness to the children. They didn't linger but rested in their cars like fat cats on the garden wall. Poverty crept up the causeway, but Mike seemed to be made of kindness. *Only the rich can afford to be nice*, Maman would shout. So become a lawyer and smile all day with no problems, but until then, don't bother trying to change her mind.

Mornings in the garden terrace, scentless flowers bubbling up from deteriorated patches. Rubble of gentility, new world forms. The paper lanterns meant that the blur-red dusk had value, to reach under the roots of ambiguity that drove migrants windswept in boxcars over Europe. More the unassuming way to hold a bundle of expired, forged documents as if no more than speaking poor. Feigning mastery over the signified other.

On this day, we celebrate our ancestors who remind us that there are no times alone. We build a world from their memories, and they remind us of futures we have yet fostered. As with the ancients, so with us. We light a candle because by this point it has become the only way we can live with them, to enact with our own bodies the motions, prayers, the very xi that flowed through their veins.

There was a time when the Buddha was travelling in a foreign land. He was asked by the keepers of the realm: What have you done to deserve entry into our land? He answered: Why, merely to seek myself. They badgered: Yet you are foreign, what answers lie here that you cannot find elsewhere? To which he spoke: That which my soul's upbringing has not contained, but which is devotedly human. Does the soul contain humanity, then, and not the substance of the gods? What is most human is at once the form of god.

Once a year they could then be parents. Red strips of paper falling, falling in the open room. Envelopes with the new year's dreams wrapped up under pulled ears and feverish pinches. Sarah dropped her porcelain doll and cried IT'S DEAD, IT'S DEAD! but couldn't cry with rice cakes and lychee staining her steel-blue lips. They were proud and clamored with the truncated motion of foreknowing. Babies are made of whispers and mother's milk. But none can remember the feeling or imagine Maman so intimate and loving. Here, blush with baijiuin, her aspiration resurrects the fire, sleeps in its warmth by the end of the night.

A whisper under silken sky.

I'm going to be like Maman one day. This place is coming to me.
But, what about Sarah?
She doesn't want any bother about it. You can tell by the way she looks when she takes tickets.
Sour grapes, she is.
I'm gonna have all the biggest guests and presidents and movies stars coming to have breakfast.

Breakfast?

Oh, yes. When this place is mine there are gonna be some big changes.

Ryan sitting, never dead enough, as Sarah explores his turgid frame with a knife. The cut breaking through patches of blue wool, finding their course of vessels by the narrow light. Hidden, above Maman and the rising smell of steel rivulets, stars just flickering in the cracked window. I imagine the derelict shopfront, made wasteful with modern appliances, a crying man-child standing over an espresso machine comforted by a naïve lover with olive skin, more beautiful than intelligent. Bamboo frames and plastic hedges where they keep the last of the savings, and just when the bombs drop over the fields outside of town who walks in the front door but the same health and safety inspector that has presided over us like a petulant minister, drunk on plum wine, with nowhere else to go.

Maman raises a book to her face. Its earthen quality, like dug soil waiting to till, is more so for the steam and sweat of her night shift. We can hear the banter downstairs, like Babel on the eve of reckoning.

Do you remember my favorite flower?
Shui! Shui! Your name, Maman.
And have I ever told you why? Well, my maman told me that the shui, though it is born of mud, earth, blossoms into beauty that even the buddha revered. It contains each of the four elements. In the air it kisses open with the fire of sunbeam and drives its roots in water instead of the earth from which it's born. Unlike any other flower, it is said to be a fallen star that brings us close to heaven and knows what's in our hearts.

Nobody seeks balance, but the lily floats knowing that its birth and life are at peace together, that the wind may blow, and sky may burn, but there is nothing that can steal its beauty. This is the grace which quiets armies and carries nations through the brink. Be at peace now, my children, for there is much to be done. Your father is not well and does not even acknowledge his sickness. Do not be stubborn. Do not lose sight of the true beauty, even if we cannot speak like this again. Remember that I am the earth that has given you life, but like the water lily, you must tread on that which has no level, and which cannot be fully calmed. I say this now to you, remember that your ancestors are present. Go to sleep. Go to the sweetest of dreams.

Tiresias Speaks – D.M. Rice (they/them)

What they don't tell you is that I was sixteen
when it happened. A walking disorientation of sweat
and cum. Oh, sure, everyone thinks they have some
kinda secret angle, but you can rely on a prophet
only as much as a bitch in heat. I mean, good luck
trying to keep them in line when the spirit takes. Hey,
any more wine, by chance?

Oy, vey. It's always Hermaphroditus this,
Hermaphroditus that. All talk and no context!
Who are we really talking about here? The Messenger,
Bringer of the Dead, mixed with, you know, Born of the Sea
Foam, Holy Jizz, I'm taking primordial elements and
the link between life and death here. All borders are
porous, by these powers combined, and life is right
fucking strange enough as it is without your having
to understand what you could never understand.
What's the use of even talking about it?

Fine, fine. So I'm walking the flock for pa.
I guess someone upstairs thought they'd have
a good laugh at me, and send me my first holy
vision. Yes, my first, don't be so incredulous. What's
a toga besides a dress with tits out, tell me that?

So, these snakes, they're there, and just fucking
madly. Curled up into a shape just like a cunt. No, I
didn't know what it was at the time, but I take my
herding staff and poke at the cunt snakes and bam!
Right, right, this was back when I had my sight. Yes
I could see the snakes fucking, yes, I poked right into
the opening and said, Pallas Athena, What in the ever-loving
fuck, I mean really? And then these slippery shits climbed up

150

my staff and bit the wood, which glowed like the punch-drunk
eyes of Delphi, and I was transformed.

Sure, most people would have freaked out,
but I was well-born, raised in the cradle of Wisdom,
and, frankly, ready for anything other than having
to keep that damn flock entertained. I was always
singing songs back then, ya know, silly little numbers
about pretty girls and holy farts. My life as a teenage
dirtbag is not on trial here, ok? So, besides the obvious
changes, like, my hair was soft and billowing, and the
contours of my body took on new significance. I ran
like hell to the closest river and checked myself out,
and immediately, dropped down right there and began
fiddling with my clit. Holy Mother of Zeus! You can't
believe what I felt then. Imagine blowing the fuzz
of a dandelion, over and over again, each individual
seed a sparklet of pleasure, but the flower keeps popping
buds, and you reach further and further inward until you
burst into an exhausted puddle of silvery fire. Plenty of
poets out there think they're hot shit because they compare
her skin to porcelain silk, it's bullshit. Unless they can get
on both knees and tell me about the throbbing, pulsing heat
of a well-worn fuck, the desperate overwhelming tremors
so deep you forget to fucking breathe, well they're either
amateurs or, you know.

After about an hour of that, I realise
that I'm taking the matter into my own hands,
when I could be out there having the real thing.
That's what Plato was really having you on about
when he's lecturing about forms and shadows on
cave walls. Why settle for self-pleasure and delusion
when the real thing is out there, waiting for you to mount

it. Of course consensually, lest you go the way of Hades!
So, I walked the pasture, picking wild blackberries, enthralled
at their curves and details. The bulbous contours reminded me
of my new cunt. No, don't worry I can say that, I asked and *they*
told me yes, I definitely can. They! *They* did! How the berries
swell up with wet juice, spilled out over your lips with gushing
delicacy. Takes me back there just thinking about it.

What were we talking about again? Right!
So walking the pastures, I come across this hot blonde
stud named Chrysanthos who was the Son of Boreas
the Elder, a friend of my father's. I always thought he was
Heaven on Earth: toned calves, broad shoulders, a tight
little ass you could sink your teeth into, always walking
around with no shirt on, making all of the scrawny punks
jealous. But even if I did think about it, and let's be honest,
I sometimes did, he was such a beefcake, I thought, he had
to be as straight as one of Apollo's golden arrows. But in this form?
Well, maybe, just maybe I stood a chance. I walked
over with all the confidence of Medusa and spoke his name.

"Hey, Chrysanthos. It sure is hot out today."

He was busy tending to the gold wheat fields of his father,
swinging his scythe wildly and hadn't noticed me.

"Oh, hello. Umm, do I know you?"

It was at that point that I realized, 'Shit!
I never thought of a name! Think fast, think fast!'

"I'm Phoebe, and I've been traveling all day
to get to Athens. Is there a bathing pool nearby
where I might be able to wash up?"

He directed me to the closest bathing pool,
between our two estates, as I had hoped. After a little
goading, I convinced him to follow me to the waters
and leave his work behind. Yes, I had converted my clothes

into a more feminine look. Maybe I just knew intuitively,
you're missing the point! This is the real saucy bit!
I dropped my gown by the river and turned around
to study his chiseled jawline further. I stepped closer
to him, whispered in his ear for him to join me and helped
pull off his toga. He did not disappoint! He dangled like a heavy
fruit on a weak vine, and the veins along his arms were fully visible.

I felt a wet heat begin to swell in me, and I threw myself at
him right then and there. His manhood pulsed to life around my
lips, and I rode him like a horse until he came in thick spurts. He
managed to pull out and everything. A perfect gentleman, truly.

After that we bathed in the pool together.
He told me that he had fun but that he was really
more into boys, that he had only laid with me
because he thought I was a goddess.
An honest mistake, but one which sent
a pang of misery deep into my soul.
Maybe if I had just asked nicely and not
been so quick to judge I would have been
able to have him without duplicity.
Maybe we could have had something real.

There were plenty of other lays,
of course, but none so exciting as that.
I crashed out at Delphi and used mulled
wine and absinthe to kill the babies
that grew in me, just like the other girls.
We smoked mugwort and sang songs,
serious, enchanting tunes about apocalyptic
visions and the folly of men.

You have to remember that I stayed
that way for seven years. Seven years of free love,
beautiful misadventure, and feminine brotherhood.

Sisterhood? You still don't understand.

One day, after a very wild weekend, hungover
like Aries on his rival's blood, I saw a lone snake slither
in the grass. Immediately I burst out laughing and cried out,
Pallas Athena, Matron of my Curiosity, share with me your wisdom
and let me see the truth. And with that, I was changed.
Not only changed, but aged, with a beard as long as you
see here today. Not only changed, not only aged, but,
wouldn't you know,
I was also struck blind.

My Body is My Own Canvas – Carella Keil (she/her)

I

I'll tell you the story. The way it really is, rough as sandpaper. My whole life is a movie. A black and white movie. Not an old-time classic, just a black and white movie. Sometimes there's red. A shimmery pinkish-red, like the color of my hair and sometimes my boots and on unexpected evenings, a violent sunset that gashes open the sky. This is mostly a silent film, a grey film. I skip along the sidewalk and walk in the gutters and suck on red lollipops and all the grey cars are parked at the curbs and the streets are utterly still and silent.

I'm not a narcissist. And I'm not color-blind. For a long time I just didn't see things in color. My senses were bleached, my emotions atrophied. Maybe that's why I needed Jasper so bad. Why I sunk my teeth in so deep and refused to let go. Why his name didn't taste like metal in my mouth. The instant I saw his eyes, I saw dandelion seeds blowing in a blue wind. I'd never seen blue before, I'd never even felt it. And I wanted it, I wanted it.

He worked at a tattoo parlor. He was twenty-eight. He had beautiful blue eyes and wavy black hair and an eyebrow ring, and he was a real fucking prick when I first met him. Maybe he still works there. Maybe he's still a real fucking prick. Maybe his eyes are stone grey now. It doesn't matter, because I still would have found a way to meet him.

* * *

I always get lost in the city, show up to class late or not at all. I always leave early, skipping down the formidable stone steps, laces untied, skirt flying and book-bag banging against my shoulder. It just feels like the time to leave, so I leave. I have a wanderlust for the city.

November is the best time to wander, the best time to skip class. No exams and the leaves whirl crisp and grey around your ankles. Sometimes I catch a silver leaf. Sometimes a silver leaf catches me by surprise, grabs my hand and drags me along the pavement. Come on. Hurry up. We're going Somewhere. And the skies, are so open in November, ribcages with no souls, I can look straight up and see heaven. I never saw any red leaves that fall. Maybe it was a sign. I would later see so much red.

II

I put my hand to the back of my head. Take it away. Sticky. Blood. Red. I lean against the wall, sink down a little lower. Rust-red bricks claw my white shirt up. The cold stone wall numbs the back of my bare legs. The wind pierces me. I lift up my skirt with one hand. Put my hand between my legs. Stare down the empty alleyway, watch dusk chase the charcoal sun. Pull my hand away. Red.

* * *

Can you look straight at the sun? Try. Feel it digging into the back of your eyes, feel it pushing into your sockets until everything is white.

This is what it feels like. When you're fourteen and you're walking home from school in the early evening and a man follows you into an alleyway. Your mom always warned you about strange men and alleyways. Your mom always warned you about drugs and sex and black cats and broken ladders. But your mom's the one who went to a New Years' party when she was 19 and swallowed a bottle of pills and glass after glass of fierce red wine until she saw nothing but white for a month. So you don't put much stock in your mother's words.

He could be nineteen, twenty. He could be your older brother. Maybe he's in college and maybe in a few years he'll ask you out for coffee or maybe a drink at a pub. Maybe his eyes are green as moss. Maybe he has a pet puppy. Maybe he sees your white stockings and tartan kilt and your gawky freckled face and he wants to turn you into a swan. Maybe he likes how you made a wreath of leaves and pinned them in your hair. Maybe he thinks you're a prostitute. Maybe he thinks you're a whore for love, touch, affection.

Maybe he's just fucking horny.

He breathes smoke into your mouth, you want to turn away and run but you're strangely mesmerized. He smiles. His lips are cracked. He pushes you up against the wall. Unzips his jeans. Pulls your legs apart, yanks them up around his hips. He bangs you up against the wall, bangs you again and again. Your head throbs. You want to remain sealed to this pain. You feel your backpack slip to the ground. For some reason, this slippage bothers you more than being raped in an alleyway only a few blocks from the nearest streetcar.

When he's done, he whispers in your ear. He's still chewing on the same cigarette. You smell blood and metal. He tells you he's sorry. Sorry he took your cherry. He looks you up and down, winks at you. Chuckles.

157

If you were older and wittier, you'd tell him you'd wear a sign next time. If you were older and wiser, you'd call the cops, a school counselor, your mother. But you are a whore for love, and the only person you want to run to is Jasper, the artist at the tattoo parlor. Because you're so sick of seeing only red.

You sink into the brick wall with your hands up between your legs and stare deep at the sun until everything is bleached white and you can feel the burn in your retinas. The word Raw comes to mind. You see red gore everywhere. A ripped heart, a punctured lung, a cigarette smashed in the street with spatters of your blood on it. You turn your head to the side and vomit. For the first time you wonder, why did mom drink so hard and deep, and what was she trying to destroy inside.

*Originally published by Empyrean Literary Magazine Issue 3: Vol. 1 No 3

If There's a Ledge to Hang From – Eliza Marley (she/her)

SeaPoint Cove was not actually a cove, but it was a point. Situated across three miles of a leveled off mountain, along the northern coast of California, a brand new Lifestyle Community was constructed. It consisted of a small neighborhood of single family homes, a main street of shops and restaurants, and a few basic amenities, like a school, a theater, and a library. What made SeaPoint Cove different from other exclusive, luxury living was their explicit promise that within 50 years the ocean levels would rise and everyone in the community would own pristine, private beachfront property.

The promise of a beautiful and exclusive beach within a lifetime was enough to get a few young families flocking up the mountain and into their new homes. One young couple, Sandy and David, used all the money they'd saved for their honeymoon on a downpayment for a house in row three out of five in the neighborhood. All of the homes were staggered row by row with large bay windows that faced out towards the beach, at least where the beach would be. For now, it faced the cliff. The cliff's edge jutted out a good quarter mile or so over the open air. SeaPoint Cove's Development Company had put up a railing right at the edge and built a large metal sign that said, "Boardwalk". All the townspeople would walk along their boardwalk and look out over their ocean. It was down there somewhere, about 8,000 feet, through the cloud bank and fog. Everyone insisted that if you walked all the way out to the very end, opened your arms, squeezed your eyes shut, and held your breath, you could hear the waves crashing down below.

Sandy and David settled into their new community fairly easily. Sandy got a job at the local library and David started working for SeaPoint Cove's Community Improvement Taskforce. It was a group of young residents who wanted to make the most of their neighborhood and really put SeaPoint Cove on the map. Their first order of business was constructing a temporary beach. Just because the real thing would take a little while didn't mean they couldn't enjoy all the activities that came with living in an oceanside town. Thirty tons of sand were airlifted in and spread around the area just south of the cliff's edge so people could still enjoy the view while they sun bathed or made sandcastles. They installed volleyball nets, lounge chairs, and a surfboard rental. The sand was contained mostly through a clever netting system underneath, and a small crew was employed to regularly sweep the edges of the beach back into order. Being so high up, windstorms were frequent. After the third volleyball net was blown right off the mountain, the Taskforce elected to stop installing new ones. They began drafting plans for a tennis court instead.

SeaPoint Cove aimed to provide an authentic, beach-town life from the scenery all the way to the shopping district. Their Main Street was lined with garlands of colorful flags and miniature lighthouse statues between the shops and restaurants. Only a few were open now, but they had plans to open more as residents continued moving in. For now, there was a seafood restaurant that boasted excellent clam chowder from fresh, airdropped clams and a sandwich shack. There was a corner store that sold swimsuits and snorkels, an old-fashioned candy shop, and a souvenir shop that sold home decor along with shirts and snowglobes. Sandy and David obtained most of their decorations from this shop. Their favorite piece was a wire and plaster seagull statue wearing sunglasses and holding an ice cream cone in one wing.

Sandy and David embraced their daily routine with dedication and enthusiasm. In the mornings, they would have breakfast and walk to work together. David was working on plans for a community center building and Sandy was teaching art classes and other programs for the sparse library patrons. When they returned home in the evening, they would cook and eat dinner together in their small, yellow kitchen. After dinner, they would go on a walk. Hand in hand, Sandy and David would circle the town and walk all the way out to the edge of the boardwalk. There, they would open their arms, close their eyes, hold their breath, and listen for the waves down below.

Sandy would let the wind whip back her hair and rush in her ears. She was sure the ocean was there, somewhere below. She would peek her eyes open while David's remained closed. All she could see were stars and the distant lights of town behind her. Sometimes she would sit in the grass, even dangle her feet off the cliff's edge in an attempt to get closer. She longed to feel the ocean spray on her fingers, hear a real seagull, anything that would tell her it was coming. All she ever got was wind.

Every so often, SeaPoint Cove would get tourists. People from small towns further down the mountain and the surrounding area would drive up to see what the fuss was about. Most of them would quickly leave, declining the townspeople's smiling offers of saltwater taffy and guided tours. SeaPoint Cove's Development Company decided the town could be more colorful, more inviting to tourists and potential homebuyers. Murals were commissioned on almost every building on Main Street and a speaker system was installed to play a soundscape of ocean waves and bird calls 14 hours a day. Trucks of delicate, beautiful flowers were brought in for residents to add to their yards. Many of the flowers died after a couple of weeks, not the right varieties equipped for the cold and windy mountain air. There were plans in the works to hire artists to construct fake flowers out of cloth and wire to replace them, possibly even open a flower shop.

One night, almost half a year into living in their new home, David noticed a dip in their kitchen floor. There was a hole, perfectly round, and about the size of his palm. Carefully, he shined a flashlight into the hole, but couldn't see anything. David found that odd, surely underneath the floor was the cement foundation all the homes were built on. Under that, he supposed there was just dirt. This was as if someone had taken a perfect, cookie-cutter chunk right out of the ground. David didn't want to be late for work, so he resolved to talk with Sandy about it later.

David wondered if the hole had been his imagination, too much caffeine from the coffee house that had opened with the newest influx of families. But when he and Sandy returned home that evening, the hole had grown to almost a foot in diameter. Still perfectly round, and perfectly dark. Sandy looked closer, sticking her hand carefully into the hole and searching for an edge, or wires, anything really. She tried lighting a match, but as soon as it went into the hole, all the light was gone. David put in a call to the Development Company's Resident Satisfaction Division, surely a hole like this spoke to greater structural issues and safety concerns. The company said they would send someone over.

The repair people came and inspected the hole. They stuck a rope with an industrial light attached inside and after they lost both the light and ran out of rope, they said they would have to come back the following week. The couple was advised to monitor the hole but to go on with life as normal. They would be back to patch it up before they knew it. Over the next week, the hole grew to about three feet in diameter and took up the center of their kitchen. Sandy made a joke about tossing their food scraps in it, but David had been annoyed with the situation ever since he had dropped his keys inside by accident. The repair team called back a few days later and said that with the high demand of building projects going on, it would take them a little longer to fix the hole and thanked them for their patience.

Word spread fast around town about the couple's mysterious hole in the floor. Neighbors started coming by, offering pitchers of lemonade and peach cobblers in order to glimpse a peek. David and his team with the Community Improvement Taskforce drafted a list of possible fixes that included nailing boards of wood across it or throwing a large rug on top of it. David tried both of these, but each time the hole spread until the obstruction was sucked inside. The hole was just over five feet in diameter now. Sandy kept testing the hole as well, shining different lights inside and even shouting out 'Hello' to see if there was a response. When she was close to the edge of the hole, she swore there was a light breeze, like a wind current gently pulling her inward.

When she told her coworkers about the hole, her friend Marta pulled her aside and asked if she could come by to see it. Sandy didn't see any harm and invited her over for lunch. Marta showed up that weekend with a pasta salad and a sealed envelope. She explained how she had lost her husband before moving to SeaPoint Cove and thought it might be nice to write him a letter. It had been sitting on her dresser at home for weeks and she wondered if she could drop it into the hole. Sandy let her, of course, and together they watched as the white envelope disappeared swiftly into the darkness. Afterwards, they ate the pasta salad and Marta said she felt like a weight had been lifted.

After Marta's visit, more people started showing up with things they wanted to throw into the hole. It was cathartic, it seemed, to toss something away into the unknown. Sandy tossed something away too. While David worked late, developing plans on a new snow cone stand to replace the one blown off the mountain, she had drawn a picture. It was of the beach she grew up down the street from, back in Michigan. She drew the dune grass and the hot, squishy sand filled with little shells and pebbles. She drew the waves, rolling in and lapping at the shore. Sandy let her picture go and watched it get eaten by the floor.

It turned out that the hole in Sandy and David's kitchen floor was the best attraction SeaPoint Cove had to offer. After Shirley, one of the other librarians, had told her grandson about the hole, he drove up with a group of his friends from Santa Barbara to try dropping things in and investigate. They made a video about 'The Bottomless Pit', posted it online, and suddenly cars filled with curious people started showing up in SeaPoint Cove. Tourists lined up to see the hole, take a picture, and toss something inside. Sandy and David were unsure at first about all the people coming into their home, but the traffic was good for the town's development, and all the extra revenue spent at the shops was going to fund a roller-skating rink.

For weeks, all day long, people would come and ring the couple's doorbell. They both had to take time off work to properly manage the flow of traffic. Families with kids would take pictures posing in front of the hole. The bravest would take pictures holding their children up and over the hole. One family had a few kids, each

164

with something to throw inside. The youngest child, a small boy clutching a teddy bear, seemed hesitant to let it go. He leaned over, trying to see where it would land, if the hole really was as bottomless as it seemed. He leaned and leaned and leaned and leaned.

After the boy and his bear, people stopped coming to SeaPoint Cove. It was mainly because Sandy and David stopped answering the doorbell. The rescue crew had left, packing up their gear and lanterns with sad shakes of their heads, too afraid to venture inside after their ropes and cameras showed nothing but darkness. The crowds outside eventually dispersed. David put in regular calls all week to the Development Company, trying to get someone to come and fix their floor. Sandy went back to work and smiled as she shelved books, but she took longer lunch breaks alone outside. Her and David still ate dinner together, but they did so in the living room instead of the kitchen. They still took evening walks too, but they didn't talk. They walked a distance apart from each other, hands stuffed in coat pockets and their eyes fixed on the flat, grey horizon.

Finally, David got a call back, but it wasn't from the repair people, it was the president of SeaPoint Cove's Development Team calling with an offer. He wanted to buy their house. It was a tragedy, he insisted, a real tragedy what happened. He wanted to take the house off their hands, remove any emotional burdens for them. SeaPoint Cove planned to convert the house and its Bottomless Pit into a landmark. They would put up a memorial for that family, of course, but such an amazing site deserved to be witnessed. In exchange, SeaPoint Cove would provide them with a new house. He told David they had been developing a new community, a premiere neighborhood of SeaPoint Cove with larger, more modern family homes. They were being built just a couple miles East of town. Plans were being drawn for a helicopter landing pad and a yacht marina once they finished leveling off the land. David thanked the man and told him they would start packing immediately. The man informed David the houses were almost finished, but to hold off packing for a few days until they were painted and ready to move in.

David went home to tell Sandy about the new house, but she wasn't there. She wasn't at the library or the sandwich shack either. He found her out on the boardwalk, all the way at the cliff's edge where the wind had blown chunks of earth off the cliff and into the sea below. The edge was narrower now, sharper too. Sandy was standing with her arms open, breath held, and eyes wide open. David took her hand in his and walked them back. He didn't let go as they walked through town together. The speakers were acting up again, static clipping in over the endless loop of wave sounds and seagull calls. They walked together, hand in hand, and David promised the new house would be a new start.

Sandy and David split a bowl of clam chowder that evening and started planning how they would decorate a bigger house.

A few days passed and David hadn't heard anything more from the Development Company. Someone had come by to inspect their current home and install a safety rope, carpeted path, and a ticket booth around the hole. Sandy and David went to work, ate their dinner in the living room, and waited for the phone to ring. They had packed most of the house away already and were quickly growing restless. The weather took an unusually rough turn. Rain and hail pounded down on SeaPoint Cove, wrecking yard ornaments and wreaking havoc on their artificial beach. Many of the building's roofs had leaks and Sandy was spending the day putting proactive covers over all the library shelves. David was home, all community improvement projects on hold until the storms passed. With nothing else to do, he put on his rain boots and coat to take a walk.

David walked East instead of through town, towards the thick and untouched woods outside of their picket fences and speaker systems. He was looking for SeaPoint Cove's new community project. Just a quick look. Maybe if the house seemed close enough to being done, David could call and inform the company they would move in as is. Afterall, he and Sandy could handle some of the finishing themselves.

David walked further into the woods that still claimed most of the mountain. He walked through tall grass, past lush ferns and wildflowers. He walked along a rushing stream filled with sparkling river rocks and jumping frogs. David felt lucky to live in such a place. Maybe they could install a zipline here over the stream.

Eventually, he came out of the woods at a clearing filled with beautiful houses. There were about eight of them, with grand, curved front doors and beautiful iron banisters. The windows were large and framed with flower boxes. Many of the homes had Victorian style torrents and sunrooms while a couple others were more modern and geometric in design. David walked closer, wondering which house would be theirs, but as he got closer, something felt off. The house fronts were so flat, the windows didn't reflect any light, and as the rain hit them they swayed. David realized they were *only* fronts. Each beautiful house was painted on large, nailed together pieces of wood and propped up in the clearing. The houses here weren't close to being finished at all. They didn't even exist.

David walked up to the wooden fronts and saw how the paint was haphazardly slapped onto the wood. Up close, they were a mess of dirt and jagged nails. He kicked the side of one, hard. He kicked it again and the wood shuddered all the way up to the top where a piece fell loose, falling into the grass. David jumped back. He watched the painted facade get battered by the storm, swaying and creaking where it stood. Some of the paint was starting to wash off, dripping down the wood and nails into muddy puddles where it sunk into the damp earth below.

When Sandy got home from work, she was alone. The storm was in full swing, pelting almost sideways against the windows. She lit a lamp and crept around the hole in the floor to make something for dinner. While she chopped peppers and onions, Sandy heard dripping from somewhere in the house. She grabbed a bowl and a few dishtowels and went in search of the leak. Sandy walked through the whole house and couldn't find anything, ending up back in the kitchen, finally noticing where the sound was coming from. The hole in the floor.

Sure enough, from the darkness Sandy could hear a faint dripping sound. For the first time in weeks, she let herself look inside the hole. Sandy sat at its edge and leaned over, still seeing nothing. She leaned further, her hair dangling into the dark. She felt the same breeze as before, similar to a drafty cave. She stuck an arm in and wiggled it around, trying to find where the drip was coming from, but still couldn't see a thing. Sandy laid on the ground on her stomach. She crawled, reached her arms and head out over the hole, and closed her eyes. She swore she felt a drop of water hit her finger when the sounds of the front door opening prompted her to pull herself back up.

David walked in soaking wet and holding a single piece of plywood in his hand. He set it on the table and laughed, a little out of breath, and wiped a wet hand across his forehead. Sandy asked him if it was time to go.

Together, they packed their remaining clothes and belongings into the final moving boxes. They left the larger furniture and stacked their boxes into the car they had driven up the mountain in. Sandy pulled her seagull statue out of the lawn and they added it to the backseat of their car. None of their neighbors came out to wave goodbye, they might not have even noticed they were leaving. Sandy and David drove out of SeaPoint Cove and back down the mountain, winding around narrow roads bordered by tall trees and wildflowers. When they finally reached the base a couple hours later the rain had stopped. They drove down a long highway with the ocean right beside them. Waves crashed up onto the beach and Sandy rolled down her window to hear them better.

*Forthcoming in *You Shouldn't Worry About the Frogs*

Willow – Jacek Wilkos (he/him)

We were walking along the road paved with good intentions when I saw a strange tree growing nearby. I went closer to take a better look.

The branches turned out to be female bodies. Rachitic hands wrapped around gnarled, dried torsos. Straight, black hair hung like leaves. I looked at my guide with a question in my gaze.

"They are the women who were terribly jealous of their husbands. They thought they were being cheated on, they didn't accept any reasonable explanations. They sought the evidence of unfaithfulness in trivial things, details which in fact meant something else, or weren't there at all.

Their delusions multiplied with time, eventually leading to a tragedy. One small spark was enough to trigger an explosion of fury and led to a crime of passion. The women were killing their husbands with anything they had on hand, inflicting multiple stab or cut wounds.

When they became convinced of the falsehood of their suspicions and realized what they'd done, they took their own lives from despair. Honest regret for sins could redeem the guilt, but the suicide squanders it. Now memories of their husbands are intertwined with visions of murders in the minds' eyes."

I looked again at the tangled souls. One of them opened her watery eyes. Two rivulets ran down her cheeks. Tears fell to the ground and disappeared, absorbed by the black sand.

Adobo Heart – Georgie Morvis (they/them)

The letter informing me Grandma had died arrived three days after her funeral. I recognized the chicken scratch of Uncle Gabriel's handwriting on the envelope immediately and ripped it open, standing in the frigid foyer of my apartment building. A few curt sentences on printer paper, listing the relevant details: old age, December 28 at Harada Funeral Home, don't bring my roommate.

My body guided me up three flights of stairs and into the apartment. Keys still swinging in the door like a metronome, I left the letter on the table and boiled a kettle for tea. I tried to convince myself it wasn't a shock. She had been near 90. A hip replacement and two knee surgeries since the hospitals reopened for non-emergency procedures. I wouldn't have been able to afford to go, anyway, cause flights to Kauai during tourist season cost three month's rent.

The last time I saw her was at a family potluck, before the pandemic. I helped with the pupus: spam musubi, mango chutney with cream cheese, lomi salmon. Aunties and uncles had brought over lumpia, pancit, shoyu poke, lechon, teri beef. But the star was her chicken adobo. So popular that she always made three pots worth, never enough for leftovers.

I sat down next to her on one of the plastic chairs haphazardly set up in the backyard. With her fingertips, she scooped up some rice off the styrofoam plate and chewed it slowly, thoughtfully, silently watching me eat. I smiled. Still the best adobo I had ever tried. I said as much. She asked me when I was bringing a girl home. My smile faded. I gulped down the chicken and opened my mouth, but Uncle Gabriel glared at me. I just forced a laugh, trying to swallow the vinegar in my voice, and said: "No time soon, Grandma."

The door to the apartment suddenly slammed shut, yanking me out of my memories and back to the kitchen. The kettle was screaming.

"Babe, what are you doing? We're having people over at 8." Ryan was taking off his coat by the door, my set of keys in his hand.

I turned to face him. I could taste tears on my lips. His face transformed instantly from confusion to sympathy. "Oh, babe."

#

We decided I wouldn't tell anyone at the party. I didn't want the questions that would come with canceling on New Year's Eve, and I didn't want the pity that would come if I told anyone why. Guests began to arrive exactly 30 minutes after the party was supposed to start. I kissed everyone on the cheek, dutifully accepted champagne bottles, and even wore the 2023 glasses that Ryan's friends insisted were ironic.

My best friend, Sofia, breezed through the door in a polka dot dress and I realized I hadn't texted her the news yet. We had shared halo-halo in Filipino Club our freshman year at Northwestern and had been inseparable since I came out to her as gay and she came out to me as Sofia. She squeezed me tight after I told her, then took my face in her hands and looked at me gravely.

"Do you want to talk to her?"

"I mean, of cou—" I started, and then I remembered. Sofia had once confided in me that she was a shaman's daughter in a long line of shaman's daughters that had survived Spanish inquisitors and American soldiers. She could communicate with the spirit world. Another secret shared, another charm on the bracelet of our friendship. I had always believed her, but I never had *believed* her.

Sofia grabbed my hand and led me to the bedroom. Ryan followed. I set my phone on the nightstand next to the jar of coins he insisted on saving. My aunties had always given handfuls of pennies and nickels to the children at New Year's Eve parties, to try and manifest good fortune for the year.

"Think of what you're going to ask her." Sofia said. "You never know how much time you'll have."

I sat down on the edge of the bed and she stood over me. Barely audible, she began to speak Tagalog in a staccato rhythm, not quite a chant but like reciting a mnemonic to remember the names of the planets. I had never learned the language, only knew a few slurs my cousins had lobbed my way.

Suddenly the air in the room felt sticky and thick. I glanced at the radiator, but its usual cacophony of whistles and groans was silent. Then, a pocket of cool air floated lazily across the room like the tradewinds. I felt it stop on my shoulders like a reassuring hand. I looked up at Sofia. She nodded.

I had nothing to say. I missed her. I missed her soft laugh, the house that seemed to spawn cousins I had never met, the colorful patches she sewed into the knees of my jeans, the plumeria trees in her front yard, and her chicken adobo—

"Do I say it out loud?"

Sofia nodded again.

"Grandma. Hi. Uh. I love you."

Love you too. It was like a thought in my head, but in her voice, in the accent she never lost. She sounded weary, like she did at the end of the nights I fought with my uncles about politics.

"Ryan, can you go back to the party?" I said quietly. He left without a word. He would have more questions than I had answers for right now. He always did when it came to my family.

"Can you teach me your adobo recipe?"

In my head she began to give me instructions. Always bone-in chicken thighs. Braise for at least an hour, but brown the chicken first, skin-side down to get it crispy. All the ingredients, including one I had never seen in the many recipes I had tried. *But you can never tell anyone.*

"I promise."

Who was that haole man you sent out of the room?

"He's my partner." I said without thinking. The room was silent for a few more seconds, then the air seemed to deflate, no longer humid nor cold but staid. Empty.

#

The next morning we rose early. Sofia and some other friends were coming over later for a lazy afternoon of smoking away our hangovers. Ryan put the empty champagne bottles and plastic cups into a trash bag while I went to the grocery store. By the time I returned it was like there hadn't been a party. Ryan was at the kitchen table, doing the crossword on his phone. His resolution for the year. I pulled out the dutch oven I had bought with my first big paycheck and got to work.

An hour later, I took the lid off the pot gingerly, peering inside, and was greeted by a blast of steam to the face. A cloud of garlic and cane vinegar and shoyu and rendered chicken fat and yes, Grandma's secret ingredient, twirled into my nostrils. I staggered backward, overwhelmed by the fragrance and disoriented from the heat, before someone's hand grabbed my shoulder. Steadied me. I looked toward Ryan, but he was still seated at the table, staring down at his phone. I felt a squeeze just like the day before, and in my head: *Give him my love.*

With the focus of someone building a house of cards I composed my plate. A heaping scoop of white rice from the 25 lb bag we had lugged back from the grocery store on Argyle. Two chicken thighs with glistening caramel skin. An extra pour of the deep brown broth, peppercorns and bay leaves fished out. An emerald dusting of furikake atop the rice.

I set the plate down in front of Ryan and handed him a fork. I ate with my hands. We shared the plate wordlessly. When the plate was clean except for two brown chicken bones, Ryan opened his mouth. Before he could speak, I leaned over and kissed him, leaving his mouth covered with adobo lipstick.

Halloween, 2000 – Charlotte Ella Rosenblum (she/her)

At one house, a little girl is scared. Not of the skeleton decoration hanging from the ceiling or the fake cobwebs in the bushes, but of the "Bush, Cheney" sign on the front lawn. Good, I've gotten my timing right. The girl's parents are embarrassed. They tell her to get her Kit-Kat bar and move along. I run past dozens of little girls dressed as princesses and devils and ghouls in white bed sheets. I'm reckless, knocking down pumpkin-shaped pails full of candy and making kids cry. I feel bad, but I have to move quickly. It can be dangerous to have bare feet on nights like these, the cold October air is blowing into my nightgown, but none of that will matter soon. I try to make out the street signs in the dark to make sure I'm in the right neighborhood. Some of the photos I've seen have "14 Orchard" on the back. I'm at the right door now, I think. I've gotten here just in the nick of time, but I think time travel often works that way. He'll be here any minute, seeing as the porch lights are on. Catching my breath, I stand under them with the moths and scan the frosted yellow windows trying to get glimpses of the interior. In one room, my mother who isn't my mother yet is in front of a vanity wearing cat ears. She applies glittery black lipstick and admires the way her skinny jeans hug her seventeen-year-old hips. In the distance, I hear the menacing growl of the engine on my father's busted Honda Civic approaching. He has come to pick her up for the party. If the stories I've been told are right, he'll be wearing his letterman jacket and he'll honk instead of knocking. She will find it endearing. She found it all endearing at first. I can see his headlights getting closer. I need to move faster. I knock on the door frantically. There's something I need to tell her.

The Juliettes – Charlotte Ella Rosenblum (she/her)

This Juliette is sitting in a room in urgent care looking at the pain scale poster on the wall. The one with the scale from 1-10 and the cartoon faces. She looks down at her hand. It's wrapped in gauze. Under the gauze, her skin is printed with a purple-red, blistering, Australia-shaped patch. She looks back up at the pain scale and whispers to herself: *about a 3*. She hadn't actually felt any pain or even really noticed when her hand was pressed straight onto the stove for five and a half seconds because she had just gotten off of a phone call. A phone call in which her boyfriend of three years dumped her without warning. Well, it wasn't that there was absolutely no warning. She could feel the signs throughout the previous few weeks. The short, cold answers to her questions that made her feel like a child begging for her parents' attention, the days without speaking, the smell of girls that weren't her on his cheek. Every time she noticed one of these signs, it felt like different parts of her body were in close proximity to fire. Places on her neck where he had kissed her were branded with a hot rod, anywhere he had held her was burning— hips were on a hot skillet, hands pressed onto the stove. Every time this happened, she immediately told herself that it would hurt so much more if she actually put her hand on a stove and she should stop being so dramatic about a teenage boy. This time, when the internal flames felt so unbearably hot and so unbearably real, she decided to test that theory. She had been wrong. The burn on her hand was a 3. Phone call with aforementioned teenage boy? A 10.

This Juliette gets in her car with burn cream, Advil, and a gnawing emptiness in her lower stomach. At 16, This Juliette has just gotten her license but feels like she shouldn't be allowed to drive. Those dimwits at the DMV didn't think to see how she would drive with a burnt hand and a broken heart. When she gets to the front of her house, she sees someone sitting on the front steps.

This is when she meets Juliette. The other Juliette.

Other Juliette is identical to this Juliette but looks a bit older, with a disposition that makes her look aged, not by time, but by circumstance. She looks like she has been running, or crying, rained on, or all three. Her mascara is in long stripes down her cheeks. Most notable is what she is wearing. A tiara attached to a veil and a long princess-cut wedding gown.

"Man. No way" says Other Juliette
This Juliette pauses and looks around her before setting her gaze back on her clone in the wedding dress
"Who are you?"
Other Juliette ignores the question, stands up, and walks down the steps past This Juliette
"Its full damn circle."
This Juliette turns around and walks faster to catch up to Other Juliette, "Huh? I'm sorry, I still feel like I need to ask because you seem nice but it kind of scares me that you kind of look exactly like me. Who are you?"
Juliette stops and sighs as if she's had this conversation before.
"Did that blonde baseball playing dick just dump you?"
"Yeah, his name is—"
Other Juliette interrupts her
"I know his name. Blonde Baseball Dick."
"Yeah, he did. Are you like me from the future or something?"
Other Juliette chuckles lightly
"Do I look that old? Not the future sweetie, a different dimension"

A different dimension in which Other Juliette was left at the altar. The altar-escaping man had been with Other Juliette for seven years. Her longest run yet. This is why Other Juliette wasn't devastated, just tired. She had done this before. Fifteen times. After that fateful day when Blonde Baseball Dick threw razor blades into her mouth through the telephone wires, she was split in half. Half of Juliette was launched into a parallel universe while the other half of Juliette stayed sixteen. Other Juliette, the half in the other dimension, has spent the last ten years doing this. Dimension hopping. Different boys, different time periods, different continents. Always the same ending. She was a lost tourist, growing increasingly wary with each failed relationship. Sure, she lost trust in men but mainly, she lost trust in herself. Because everything that felt like love was not even close. She felt it slow-dancing under the stars with what's-his-name from Argentina. What's-his-name from Argentina felt the six glasses of wine. She felt it with the boy who whispered to step on his shoulders to climb up to his roof on the 4th of July because there was no ladder, his parents were asleep, and he wanted her to see the fireworks. The boy felt it too, until one day he didn't. Then, of course, she felt it on her wedding day. She felt it more than she had ever felt anything. The groom felt claustrophobic. He must've, seeing as he jumped out of the dressing room window and ran four miles in his tuxedo as the wedding march began to play.

She tells all of this to Juliette. This Juliette, this sixteen year old Juliette who has just been burned for the first time and was really hoping it would be the last. This Juliette, who until this point thought it was dramatic of her to think that maybe there was just something inherently unlovable about her. Something off with the chemistry in her mother's womb or something sour laced into her blood. This Juliette, who now feels like she's been proven right.

This Juliette takes the hand of Other Juliette, feeling an overwhelming sense of familiarity that puts a nauseous ache in her stomach. When Other Juliette squeezes This Juliette's hand, she can feel the burn on her hand pulse and she winces slightly. Noticing this, Other Juliette turns her hand over to show This Juliette the faded Australia-shaped continent on her hand too. Broken and put together fifteen times over, all of her scars have faded with time.

An hour later, the neighbor across the street mowing his lawn stops in his tracks. He stares blankly at the scene in front of him. Hand in hand, the Juliettes walk together down the streets labeled with signs they both recognize. Other Juliette drags a giant trash can behind her. This Juliette holds a lighter and a few rolls of toilet paper. They're on their way to Blonde Baseball Playing Dick's house.

NON-FICTION

Geometric Proof: The Immigrant's Edition – Karen Gonzalez-Videla
(she/her/hers)

Instructions: You were born in Buenos Aires, Argentina, and currently reside in Florida, United States. Complete the proof that best indicates those two statements can coincide.

<u>Statement</u>: I was born in Buenos Aires, Argentina, daughter to a Cuban mother and an Argentinian father.
<u>Reason</u>: Given (please see birth certificate for details).

<u>Statement</u>: I left Argentina on March of 2011.
<u>Reason</u>: Given (please see passport and other attached documentation for details).

<u>Statement</u>: I never really thought of the United States when I was a child.
<u>Reason</u>: That's a lie. I thought of it that time my sister and I played with worn-out barbie dolls, their hairs tangled halfway through a braid, their skirts sewed from mom's dismembered nightgowns.
   "No suenan argentinas," mom said. Barbies say *tu eres;* we say *vos sos.* We found it simple. We:

1. Never caught *vos sos* on Disney Channel.
    a. We mixed Gabriella Montez's voice with Ally Dawson's, tried to guess which dubbing voices skipped across shows like mixtapes.
2. Clicked español on movie language screens.
    a. *Tu eres* is universal.
    b. *Vos sos* is not.

   "Es que las criaron los estadounidenses," I say to mom. "Las compraron y las hicieron famosas."

My sister nods. We untangle doll hair with our hairbrush, paint their lips with red school marker. We need to get them ready for that movie premiere, the one they have all heard about, all the way from North America.

Statement: I can speak English.
Reason: I used to get tongue-tied saying "child."

"Cheeld," I said.

Mom chuckled. "Creo que se dice 'chiled.'"

I took notes on crumpled paper, bounced the word from side to side within my head.

Statement: I've called this country home since March of 2011.
Reason: I've lived in Florida since the mentioned date. I:

1. Grew my first pimple here.
   a. I inspected it in the bathroom mirror, held it between my fingers until it popped.
2. Cried in the girls' room stall of P. Middle School for 10 consecutive minutes.
   a. That was when I realized *beach* wasn't pronounced like *bitch*, when that boy behind my back said, "she probably can't tell the difference."
3. Held my head between my knees.
   a. I heard that if you squeeze hard enough, the headache might help you internalize the phonetics.

Statement: I've called this country home since March of 2011.
Reason: I think I've already proven this statement (please see above).

Statement: I can speak English.
Reason: I majored in English at university, memorized words and symbols and made them mine.

Statement: I was born in Buenos Aires, Argentina.
Reason: I believe I have already proven this statement. Please, see above.

Statement: I have never returned to Argentina ever since having left.
Reason: Sometimes I wish I had, if only to savor those *vos sos* thrown around homes, around supermarket stores, around non-Disney Channel Spanish songs.

Statement: I can speak English.
Reason: I think I've proven this statement twice already. (If you truly want the proof, see above).

Statement: I speak English more often than I speak Spanish.
Reason: That's a lie. I mix and mangle languages like ingredients on my family's chicken stew.
1. "Pass me some of those *papas.*"
2. "No te olvides de comprar el *shaving cream.*"
3. "Si no, *whatever,* a mi me que me importa."
        Nada me importa.
                Nada me importa.

Statement: I was born in Buenos Aires, Argentina.
Reason: Please, I'm begging you, I have already proven this statement. See above.

Statement: I'm the daughter of a Cuban mother and an Argentinian father.
Reason: Please, see above.

Statement: I left Argentina on March of 2011.
Reason: See above.

Statement: I can speak English.
Reason: See above!

Statement: I never really thought of the United States when I was a child.
Reason: SEE ABOVE.

Statement: I've called this country
                                        Home (?)
Reason: since   I was   eleven
                        can't you just   SEE
AVOBE
                sorry I meant   AVOVE
                                        ABOBE
                                            ABOVE

186

Isn't it funny how words lose their meaning the more that you say them? The more that you spell them?

PLEASE SEE ABOVE
ABOVE
ABOVE
ABOVE
ABOVE
ABOVE
ABOVE
ABOVE
ABOVE
ABOVE

32 – Glendalee Diaz (she/her)

I grew up with an awareness of my body from an early age. I can't remember the exact age I was when this awareness came about but I knew I was younger than 10 and mami didn't like it. You see, I was raised Pentecostal. Real strict. Long jean skirts. No earrings. No pants ever. Inside or outside the church. The type of church that didn't even let you wear sneakers on Sunday.

But I was young when I realized that my body was the topic of discussion before I even knew what my body was capable of doing. And the reason why I mention church was because for 17 years of my life that was all I knew. I lived and breathed church, not even understanding why but knowing it was something that our family just did. And I loved it. I loved the structure, the routine, the friendships that lasted years, and I loved the drama—because, yeah, even in church it was like the telenovelas on Univision and Telemundo the viejas at church used to warn us not to watch.

But at church I also became aware that eventually I would grow into a woman. That my body was something that I should not put on display. That the changes that were occurring in my body were something that I shouldn't be talking about. I didn't understand at the time how my body was something that could tempt even the holiest of men off altars, but apparently it could. And that was somehow my fault. Because we shouldn't have worn that skirt or that shirt that was too tight or too low cut in the first place. We had to maintain appearances.

I've avoided writing about church in the past because I never wanted to taint the name of the Lord, because I never had a problem loving the Lord even though I was bad at it. The expectations that the church placed on us girls at such a young age put a lot of pressure on me. It made me feel like I always had to be better than the other girls in my church, prettier, smarter, funnier, because I had to be the one that would be chosen. It was like a competition, the one where I would find my soulmate whether it was the boys already attending our church or the new boys that would visit our church. It was always ingrained in my mind that my goal was to find the person that the Lord had picked for me and I would live happily ever after, loving my husband, being the perfect Christian wife.

I was 9 years old when I had my first boyfriend in church, but at this age, I was already planning our future because that's what I would always hear the older girls talking about. Granted I was young and the way I remember this is probably not the exact same way it happened, however, this was what I remember taking into my teenage years: that my purpose in life was to marry and have babies and serve the Lord. And I sit here writing this a week before my 32nd birthday because I am turning 32 years old and I'm still unmarried and childless—two things I'm not quite sure how to feel about. In some way I feel like I failed my mother, for not living up to the expectations that she had for her three daughters. And another part of me is just like fuck it. I haven't given my parents a grandchild and if children are something that I will be blessed with in the future, my parents will most likely not be here to experience that, and it makes me wonder if having a child is even worth it.

I remember being 12 and wanting to be a grown up. I remember how I envisioned my future, being so uncomplicated, with financial security, but the reality is that being in your 30s during this time kind of sucks and having a house and a good savings account is a goal that is not impossible but feels impossible.

I read somewhere that the 30 year olds today are paving the way for the 20 year olds because we are not creating the traditional family life that was expected of us, especially in the Latin community. My mother had two kids before she was 22 and then two more before she was 33. My grandmother Mama Luz had 11 kids. I can see the worry in my mom's eyes when we talk about my future and I tell her that I do not see kids in my future, not because I do not want them, but because the way the world has turned out for me as an adult makes it hard to envision myself as a mother. But mami wants me to have kids because when she is gone, she wants to know that I am taken care of. I haven't looked too far into my future, thinking about mami and papi being gone, because that is something that is still too raw and scary to think about.

Thinking about the changes that my body has undergone from a child to a young girl to a woman is also something that I am still trying to learn to accept and love about myself, so thinking about birthing a child freaks me out as well—like can my hips get any bigger from what they already are?

And what I guess I'm trying to get across is: were we all supposed to have it figured out by now? Maybe. Maybe not.

Walking the River Path – Emily Levang (she/her)

At four, my son only sees the good in this place. I look out at the full river bending, where lush green islands meld into the opposite shoreline, merging the landscape between Minnesota and Wisconsin. We take the old railroad path along the estuary, breathing buttercup as it mingles with decaying leaves. He runs ahead, flapping his arms like a bird.

Behind us, the mouth of the river meets the harbor, flowing into Lake Superior—the sweet water sea. So much of our whole world's fresh water. Up ahead, the abandoned US Steel Mill is hidden behind trees, not easy to see. But I know—here we all know how it looms. Just one of dozens of toxic hot spots in the St. Louis River Estuary, these waters of my childhood. I've walked this path many times.

"This way!" Ronan spots a side trail going up, away from the water. "It's so magical in here!" He ducks under a canopy of aspen and birch. I follow him up the hill, words caught in my mouth as I feel what's coming. But the chain link fence doesn't strike the same chord of shock in a four-year-old, as it did for me at twelve. When he sees our way is blocked, he turns to look back at me, puts on his fierce superhero face, and gathers up his arms to fly around it.

"I'm sorry Ronan, we can't go in there," My voice sounds surprisingly flat for all that churns within me. The fence surrounds a Superfund site, blocks from my middle school. This is the most widely contaminated site on all the Great Lakes Rust Belt. To this day, the human exposure status is "not under control."

"Yes we can! We're going to see that moss," he says, pointing just inside the fence at a patch of deep green. We live on the East side of town now, where the income is higher and there are no toxic spills. He's not used to these limits.

I wonder how to explain this to my child.

"You know how we see litter in the woods—" Lately he's been passionately cleaning up litter, so I attempt analogy. I tell him that this place is like that, but so much bigger, with so much more damage, and that no one can ever pick it up, though many people who love this place have been trying for years.

"Why would someone hurt this land?" His question swells the ache in my chest, and I opt for the concept of ignorance, though the rage I feel wants me to speak of greed. I tell him (and myself) it's ok to feel our feelings. I've walked this path many times.

I wonder when I'll tell him that these abuses of the past are small in comparison to the threats that lay ahead. I wonder when we'll draw the line. And I wonder if we will still walk here when he is my age.

There are two paths here, now, in the present. Two divergent futures, among all the possible futures. On one path, many people are silenced. On the other, our voices rise. Here, now in the present, where these futures converge, we have a choice.

They say we need jobs. They say we need copper. Stories are spun by those who can afford to tell them, our minds fill with confusion, apathy.

I imagine one possible future: On this path, those in power have learned nothing from the past. They allow a sulfide-copper mine to be built upstream. And then another, and another, and another. Until there is a 100-mile corridor of extreme extraction through Northern Minnesota's forest and wetland, treaty land.

PolyMet is first, knowing it has a 100% likelihood of failure. Knowing those who build it have already destroyed other waterways, moved on to the next.

Many of us try to stop it, with all the means given to us; we sign the petitions, we call our legislators, we support those in court fighting the permits, and when the time comes, we gather, march, handcuff ourselves to heavy machinery. My child grows up in this fight.

But still, the PolyMet dam is built on top of an old taconite dam, half a century old and leaking. Over years, the pile of hazardous waste builds up into the shape of a pyramid on top the dam.

It's spring, and this year the unpredictable rains of climate change are like monsoons. We are sleeping in our homes, this night when the rain is so heavy it sounds like we must be underwater.

The PolyMet dam was not designed for this kind of rain. Without warning, the decrepit structure is no longer strong enough to hold up the pile. It collapses all at once.

The plume travels hundreds of miles into the watershed, carrying arsenic, asbestos, lead, and mercury. All lethal to the animal, human, plant, and waterbody. Toxic sludge churns through sacred waters, a deep blue river turns gray with death.

That morning we hear the news, watch in horror, our hearts in shreds. This will never go away. All the efforts at past remediation gone in one moment. Everything gone.

I walked this path in my mind too many times, so many I had to turn, instead, toward a prayer, a different path.

On this second path, another possible future, mid-summer is vibrant green fullness, and together my grown son and I walk this trail, toward what used to be US Steel. That place where iron that was mined up north was processed into metal, shipped all over the US so people could have nails and frying pans. A place that reminds us of the past.

As the shore curves, we see a fishing boat heading back toward the marina, nets full of walleye for one of the small-scale sustainable fishing operations. Offshore, the green arms of wild rice stalks sway in the breeze, sending a message, "this place is a good place." Later in the season, they'll be harvested, their life a sign of healing.

We follow a short offshoot from the main trail, down to the water's edge, where a circle of gray stones and small wooden benches designate one of the spaces for ritual. I bow, dipping my hands into the cool water, the water who carries the numina of so many prayers, and pour it over my head.

A child's laughter rolls down from the hill above me, in the edible schoolyard, where an elder and three elementary students are kneeling together, patting the base of a small apple tree they've just planted.

Even with the abundant garden, that hill always looks naked to me now, no longer sheltered in trees. Decades of climate destabilization brought prairie where there used to be dense forest.

This shoreline would be nearly unrecognizable, visually, yet my heart feels the same swirl of tenderness. I've walked this path many times.

On this path, those of us who care for this place remember, and we grieve. We have been grieving now, all these years. For the fish who will never return, for the spotted salamander, for the Original People. We feel all there is to feel, about what has come before us, what has been lost, and what we long for. We use our voices to invoke a different future, even in the face of all those who continue to ridicule this way.

At first it was just a few people who came, each in their own ways, to see that we *are* nature. Our bodies are the earth-body. Some received this teaching, unbroken, against all odds, from their own Indigenous lineage. Others heard whispers from the trees. And some, later, received this message from kin at workshops, rallies, ceremonies, or that one teacher at school with a glimmer in their eyes.

We continue back on the trail, toward Morgan Park, past the beloved sandy beach. A group of teenagers are splashing, pushing each other, squealing. I remember the year they officially removed the "do not swim" sign.

We can tell we're nearing the entrance to the trail that leads to the Superfund site because we begin to see offerings. Flowers, little altars made at the base of what trees are left. Art, ephemeral, made by children; garlands, cloth flags with hearts, "we love you, river."

Offerings to the ancestors of this land; the four-leggeds, the fliers, the stones, the Original People; the Dakota, Anishinaabe. Even offerings to the settler ancestors, including my son's great grandpa, who shoveled molten iron here, for US Steel, all his life.

We pause, taking a breath.

I remember the day we heard the news: PolyMet is over. The tears of relief I cried that day were bigger than this one victory. I knew then, and see clearly now: that was the beginning, the seed, of many more people coming to see, at first like peeking into a small hole into another world, eventually a wide-open view: the river is alive, she has her own right to life, and we are her. Water is life.

There are no sulfide mines in operation. Daily we give thanks for the water. We celebrate the estuary, and most unexpectedly, we've come to celebrate one another.

On this path, we don't have all the answers and we can't just fix what was harmed. But we come here, to this place. We no longer look away; we are no longer silent. We now recognize that we humans have the sacred duty to care for this place.

Sources

- https://www.epa.gov/great-lakes-aocs/st-louis-river-aoc

- https://www.health.state.mn.us/communities/environment/fish/techinfo/newbornhgl sp.html

- https://static1.squarespace.com/static/587176b720099e63d3423b7a/t/5be8dfd7f950 b7a8d8c91d3f/1541988311761/Likelihood+of+Water+Pollution+Report.pdf

- https://earthworks.org/wp-content/uploads/2012/08/Porphyry_Copper_Mines_Track_Record_8-2012.pdf

- https://www.minnpost.com/earth-journal/2015/02/canadas-worst-mine-disaster-grew-dam-built-wrong-place/

Rage, Ignorance, Love – Sydney Lea (he/him)
—in mem. Stephen Arkin (1942-2021)

I. *Rage*

I'd set out on a short hike along a trail our family has trodden clear
over decades. I paused for no reason to study an oak—likely not all
that young, just slender from having developed, acorn to tree,
beneath a canopy of pine. I had unwittingly passed this survivor
hundreds of times, no more eye-catching than any random
hardwood along that familiar mile, as unremarkable as some
stranger's face in a crowd.

But when I looked the little oak over from earth to crown,
pondering all that had transpired within its span of life on our land, I
swear I foresaw that something inside me would soon be changing.
Or did I? I honestly can't say. Memory, even recent, can be a
whimsical editor.

In that tree's time, there had been children raised here, grown now,
moved on. Not so long before, two had married beside our reed-
lined pond, and seven grandchildren, their older siblings' kids, had
burst into the world. I have a picture of those youngsters gathered
around me, the eyes of each reflecting the candles on my 77th
birthday cake.

I have raced forward thirty years from my late forties, when we
moved cross-river from New Hampshire to this chunk of Vermont. I
have moved—no, have hurtled from what I didn't know back then
was youth to an age when too many friends are losing hold. My
beloved friend Steve, for instance, had been like my own blood
from years before my family ever settled here. Now he was fatally ill

with duodenal cancer, but the hateful pandemic prevented me from visiting him as his life ebbed.

Suddenly my cell phone rang. A miracle! It works almost nowhere in this rustic region, and if I carry it into the woods at all, it's by mistake. Through her sobs, I caught the voice of my dear friend's daughter. *You have to talk to my dad right now!*

That sentence will live inside me forever.

The disease had drawn its winning card at last. Stunned, I slumped to the ground as he offered his farewell. I envisioned his face as he struggled for words: *This is hard...*

Steve soon stopped for want of breath, and I began a speech I'd been rehearsing for some while—which collapsed, of course, into incoherent blubbering. The call ended when his daughter took the phone again and, choking on her own sorrow, simply breathed, *Good-bye.*

Good-bye indeed—to a man of whom I knew so much: what made him laugh or cry, what music he craved, what food. His every defining physical gesture and turn of phrase were etched into my being. He'd read my poems. I'd read his essays and books, I hope with similar sympathy.

The small oak I'd been contemplating was uninvolved, of course, in Steve's demise, but it would go on living, despite the darkness looming above it, and, enraged by that, I imagined fetching an axe and chopping the damned thing down.

II. *Ignorance*

Next day, despite a mizzling, I went in search of that oak, but I carried no axe or saw.

I'd believed the tree would be seared onto my consciousness, but now the puny thing proved difficult to find among so many kindred whips. Something had hidden it from me. Mystified, I tramped back and forth until a sudden wind summoned cracks and groans from the forest. I got a notion. It made no more sense than being enraged by one nondescript tree among thousands. The gale felt like a reprimand for my blaming its disappearance on some invisible agency.

Needless to say, the idea of some supernal power's rebuking me was absurd. Even if such a fantastical force existed, after all, would it waste time with the meager likes of me or the oakling? And yet, at that very moment, the tree appeared. Was there some magical immanence around me after all?

Who would have thought a tree not much more than head-high could spawn the reactions I had after hearing my treasured friend's waning breaths? Now it had stepped forward again.

What followed was no likelier. Steve and I were college professors for decades, and now my oak unaccountably steered me back fifty years. Racked by nerves, I tried to lead a discussion of Milton's *Paradise Lost.* I telephoned him to report how anxious that teaching assignment had made me. His response was lighthearted, "Can't help you. He's not talking to a Yid like me."

This much later on, I truly absorbed a lesson I'd grasped only by way of intellect in that classroom. During the famous debate in Hell, spirits

> *fallen from Heaven sat on a Hill retir'd,*
> *In thoughts more elevate, and reasoned high*
> *Of Providence, Foreknowledge, Will and Fate,*
> *Fixt Fate, free will, foreknowledge absolute,*
>
> *And found no end, in wand'ring mazes lost.*

I'd be in for hellish confusion myself should I start, like those idiot devils, to ponder ultimate things. And it had been madness, particularly, to resent a mere tree.

III. Love

I sat on the stump of a yellow birch that I had in fact cut down for firewood a decade before, and I watched my oak completely shed the guilt I'd preposterously assigned to it. The stiff breeze purged the mist, and the trunk's surface, bathed now in sun, burst into every hue of the spectrum, from red at the base to violet at the crown. I didn't imagine such transformation. I beheld it.

A cluster of mushrooms gathered around the trunk was also swathed in brilliance and another memory supervened. At a certain New Haven diner in our first graduate school days, we ordered mushroom omelets one Sunday morning. The waitress, perhaps as old as I am now, asked, *caps or stems?* We sensed a wryness: eyebrows lifted, she was poking subtle fun at the eatery's affectation in offering such a choice. Every time Steve and I returned to that place, we'd wait for however long it took for one of her tables to be free. And we never varied our orders—caps, of course—just as she, clearly amused, never altered the rite.

Or rather, she did just once. After a summer's absence from town, we sat at our usual spot. Then we waited for what seemed a full minute. The woman mutely stood there, thin as a blade, pad and pencil quivering in her hand. Her eyes held not a smile but bone-weariness and pain.

At uncomfortable length, in chorus, we said *caps.*

That was the last time we saw her. We'd later learn of her own cancer.

And next I recalled another 1960s moment, the two of us high on home-grown weed. Just before we headed off to some much-lauded visiting scholar's lecture, we'd been listening to Muddy Waters's "Long Distance Call." The visitor was gushingly introduced, but before he could begin his talk, Steve stood and shouted the song's raunchy double-entendre: *Another mule is kickin' in your stall!*

The outburst was so utterly out of context in that highbrow hall that no one knew how to respond, and no one did. After a long pause, the lecture simply began, but by then Steve and I were laughing our way out the door. We called each other Muddy ever after.

These random memories had no special value—except that they did and do. Like all the others.

Once again, I invoked Milton's ruined devils. How could I possibly have foretold that their fervent philosophical blather would constitute an anti-ideal for me as Stephen Arkin lay dying in California?

I'd waste no strength on conjecture. I'd discover no justification for so shattering a loss. Instead, my thoughts moved from Milton's fallen angels to his human beings—likewise fallen, just as Steve was, I am, every one of us is.

> *The World was all before them, where to choose*
> *Thir place of rest, and Providence thir guide:*
> *They hand in hand with wandring steps and slow,*
> *Through Eden took thir solitarie way.*

The oak still clung to its polychromic glow.

*contains excerpts from Paradise Lost – John Milton

The Secret I Keep from My Mother – Francesca Leader (she/her)

My mother and I never got along when I was young. I began to resent her, early on, for her toxic parenting methods, which included spanking, slapping, emotional manipulation, fault-finding, and bribery. Before I reached the age of 25, I felt little love and a great deal of anger toward her. I often said, during arguments, that I hated her, and there were many times I truly felt that way. What I couldn't forgive was the perverse satisfaction she seemed to derive from setting me up to fail and then punishing me. I didn't understand at the time that my mother's toxic parenting was, in fact, the product of her sincere effort to avoid succumbing to alcoholism, a disease that had plagued her father, and seriously marred her own childhood. The unintended result of this noble effort was that my mother slid into a different, but no less corrosive, form of addiction: instead of alcohol, she became addicted to rage.

Throughout my childhood, I remember my mother only as one of two ways: angry or sad. We know today that depression manifests in both of these forms—outward and inward-turning. When my mother's depression turned outward, she was angry at me; when it turned inward, she was sad. Of the two conditions, she much preferred to be angry, and often seemed to seek pretexts for that anger. At least when she was angry, she could be productive. When she was sad, everything stopped.

When I was 10 years old, another mother figure entered my life. My father introduced me to his new girlfriend, a kind and beautiful red-haired woman. She was the first person he'd dated since getting divorced from my mother the previous year. I'd never met anyone like her. She was soft-spoken, patient, an amazing listener, and never rude to anyone, no matter how badly they behaved—myself very much included. My stepmother's mother—another positive force in my life—once said of me, "That's the naughtiest child I've ever seen." It speaks to my stepmother's strength of character that this remark never made it back to me until many years later, when I was old and wise enough to laugh about it. In her first years with my dad, I remember my stepmother implementing a sticker-based system of rewarding desired behavior—washing dishes, cleaning up after myself, using good manners, etc. While it didn't exactly transform me from a fridge-emptying, banister-sliding, potted plant-overturning menace overnight, it certainly taught me the value of positive reinforcement. Later in life, I would call upon this lesson in my own parenting.

Before I reached my late twenties, I didn't know if I'd ever want a child of my own. Despite the loving, supportive example my stepmother had set, I believed my mother's negativity had poisoned me, made me (probably) incapable of raising another human being without damaging it. I feared that all her toxic parenting methods would reemerge in me. I couldn't stand being around small children then—I found them noisy, needy, bothersome. I saw them as parasitic little creatures that drained your energy, kept you from doing the things you wanted. Then suddenly one night, I had a dream. A dream of a beautiful, smiling baby, and a feeling of boundless, unconditional love. When I awoke from that dream, I knew I was ready. I had my first child, a daughter, about a year later. I'm glad I made that choice.

I don't remember when I decided to start calling my stepmother "mom." I think it was in my late teens or early twenties, before I got married or had kids. I remember asking her, on a phone call, if it was OK for me to call her "mom," and she said of course, and we both cried. I also remember that my mother, when she found out about it, was not pleased. To this day, it upsets her, which is unfortunate, but understandable—I think I, too, would feel a twinge if one of my children decided to have me share the "mom" title with another woman. If that ever happens, though, I'll respect the choice, having once made the same one myself.

Even more than the fact that I call my stepmother "mom," which my mother knows, there's something else, a secret between my stepmother and me which, if I ever told my mother, would upset her terribly. Not long after my first child was born, I shared an important revelation with my stepmother: that without her influence in my life, I would never have dared become a mother, because I would've lacked any conception of what positive mothering could look like. Even when I was unsure of whether or not I wanted kids, I knew I never wanted become the bitter, abusive kind of mother that, before the age of 10, was the only kind I'd ever known. My stepmother, in other words, was the one who unlocked the well of maternal love inside me. For that, I am forever grateful to her, and I'm glad I told her—she deserved to know.

It saddens me that my stepmother and I must carry this secret between us. But to reveal it to my mother would, I think, be cruel and self-serving. My mother knows she made mistakes raising me, and I (with the benefit of hindsight) know those mistakes were unintentional. My mother was herself a victim, perpetuating the effects of intergenerational trauma, despite her best efforts to the contrary.

In recent years, my mother and I have become quite close. We talk on the phone almost daily. She shares my sense of humor, my taste in literature, my delight in beautiful things. In truth, there's a great deal of my mother in me, and most of it's good stuff. I still find it hard to share a living space with her—in-person visits usually sour after a day or two—but I also find it hard now to go even a few days without hearing her voice.

I feel fortunate to have lived long enough to appreciate my mother as I do now. She's much more than just the woman who gave birth to me. She's a complex and interesting person. She's funny, generous, a talented artist, and a great cook. She's one of my best friends. And I know she loves me. More importantly, I know she always did love me, even if she didn't know how to show it. She wasn't taught how to show it. But over time, I think she's learning.

What No One Told Me About Glitter – Lauren Emily Whalen
(she/her)

1. Glitter sticks.
2. I am dead serious.
3. That shit *fuses to your skin.*
4. I did my first professional burlesque gig in 2013. Since then I've moved apartments four times, started and left jobs even more times, and stopped performing burlesque. However, if I do enough digging, I can probably find the exact glitter that fell off my ass that Friday night before Memorial Day.
5. That glitter was iridescent, more of a sparkling powder really.
6. Before I started burlesque nine years ago I was very basic with my glitter.
7. I had no idea that for burlesquers, glitter is a fucking *science.*
8. I would learn.
9. Pre-burlesque, my glitter-wearing mostly happened in the late 90s, for dance recitals held on Memorial Day Weekend at my central Illinois hometown's public school auditorium. It was a silver aerosol spray we'd pass around from Walgreens or Sally Beauty Supply. I took ballet, tap, jazz, and modern with a lot of cheerleaders and pom squad gals, so they were better versed in glitter than I, the Catholic school nerd.
10. By the early 2000s, the dance studio banned body glitter. I think the little kids were getting into it and parents were getting mad.
11. Probably just as well—aerosol vapors and all.
12. At one point when I was home from college, my sister and I shared a small pot of body glitter, or maybe I just stole it

from her. The same size as one of those tiny pots of lip balm that were everywhere in the late 90s/early aughts, containing a gooey clear substance with tiny silver moons and stars. Probably came from Claire's. It felt sticky when I smeared it on my shoulders and arms, a thin second skin under my white blouse during the entire community theater production of *Fiddler on the Roof*. And those moons and stars would cut into my skin if I rubbed it on too hard. Tiny beads of tiny blood.

13. Glitter can be *sharp* when you don't expect it.
14. Much like burlesque dancers.
15. Anyway, back to my first burlesque gig—which, when you think about it, is like a dance recital, only with partial nudity.
16. I'm sure I poofed on my glitter that wasn't really glitter while frantically running through dance steps in my head, arranging my costumes on a black folding chair and trying not to get in anyone else's way.
17. As a baby burlesquer, glitter was the last thing on my mind.
18. Not for long.
19. For one thing, my stage name was Emma *Glitter*bomb.
20. Therefore, it stands to reason that I'd become familiar with the ins and outs of glitter: acquiring, application, and removal.
21. That last one is a bitch.
22. First up, acquiring.
23. What no one told me about glitter is how many kinds exist, how many places there are to buy it, how glitter is everywhere once you know where to look, in tiny tubes, in glass bulbs, in plastic containers like what you buy salt in at the grocery store.
24. There's no right or wrong place to get your glitter. Of course, everyone has opinions on types of glitter (bigger is

better, more visible) and where to buy (*not* the drugstore, too basic), but I stay open minded when it comes to scoring sparkle. At least, I try.

25. That first night, it was vanilla atomizer sparkle puff from The Body Shop. The gentlest, lightest feeling as I awkwardly reached behind myself and squeezed the bulb onto my bare ass cheeks. I remembered when I was three or four and longed to do that with my grandmother's perfume bottles, lined up precisely on her dresser, all pink and pretty. To clarify, I wanted to do that on my *wrists*, not my ass cheeks, possibly because the latter was never an option.

26. The sparkle powder didn't itch or stick and it smelled good, so what was the problem?

27. The problem was the powder's distinct lack of sparkle: the barest hint of sheen on my pale skin. So instead of two pale globules of derrière, I had two pale globules of derrière that were slightly shiny.

28. As with burlesque, it didn't take me long to want more.

29. For one year, I was in two troupes: "nerdlesque" parodies of film and TV and a "classic" troupe that is pretty much what you think of when you think of burlesque: sequined gowns, feather boas, music that goes *waaa waaa*. I alternated rehearsals, performances, theaters and styles by the day, the week, occasionally the hour.

30. Maybe I wanted more from the beginning.

31. Once I realized I wanted to *shine,* I progressed to the LUSH body bar.

32. The LUSH body bar is a magical product. Formed like a bar of soap that is shaped like a pair of lips, it even comes in its own oval-shaped silver tin, so you *know* it's high class.

33. The LUSH body bar emits a light perfumed scent of marshmallows and dreams.

34. The LUSH body bar is the off-white of a tulle gown in a Grimms fairy tale, pre-bloodshed, or a Hallmark Christmas movie post-makeover.

35. The LUSH body bar can go anywhere and everywhere on your person: bountiful derrière, depths of cleavage, apples of cheeks, for a dewy, ethereal countenance.

36. Best of all? The LUSH body bar *moisturizes*, which is especially helpful in Chicago winter, when public and private lips are cracked and hidden under wool until it's Saturday night and everything's just...out there.

37. The LUSH body bar is worth every minute you have to spend in actual LUSH where the salespeople are like hawks, and you know they're just doing their job, but must they be so aggressive, also the smells pretty much scream: "I will knock you and your nose on their collective behinds."

38. This was before I started shopping online.

39. For a long while, I used the LUSH body bar on its own, and I shone bright like a diamond onstage or at least it felt that way. Plus, my skin was so soft.

40. Two years in, I started layering my glitter: LUSH body bar on bottom, more sparkle on top.

41. A dancer named Rosie Roche worked at a costume shop in one of the city's toniest neighborhoods. Eventually she figured that a small plastic container with a pump that the shop sold was ideal for spraying on this type of glitter. She bought up the empty pump containers and sold them to us for four bucks each. I got one for myself and one for a woman in the troupe whose husband died of a mysterious illness after three months of marriage. I never told her it was from me.

42. I reached a point in burlesque—late 2016, three years into my career—in which I desired more on top of more.

43. Behold: craft glitter.

44. Craft glitter is the grandaddy of glitter. The silver, gold and red that's a step above powder, that I used during countless grade school art projects, that inevitably spilled all over the backseat of my parents' blue Chevy, because I used way more than the Elmer's glue would hold.

45. Then there's big craft glitter, each granule about the size of a red pepper flake.

46. Guess what: burlesque dancers buy craft glitter in bulk! Likely, we're up there with kindergarten teachers in keeping the craft glitter industry afloat.

47. The best place for me to buy craft glitter was the Michaels three blocks away from my apartment, a giant mecca for "I wanna make that."

48. I am not a crafty type, but now I find Michaels weirdly comforting. Go figure.

49. What brought me to Michaels and craft glitter was *The Buttcracker*, a holiday burlesque takeoff on the classic ballet, in which I was cast as Russian Vodka and I decided this act, which I would create myself, required a jeweled flask full of glitter attached to my head, that I would detach from my head and pour on myself at the end of the number. While in the splits.

50. Audiences go *apeshit* for splits.

51. I heard through the burlesque grapevine—a complex web of social media posts, DMs, and backstage whispers—that Martha Stewart craft glitter was the most visible, versatile, and valuable. Off to Michaels I went, pulling my peacoat around me and traversing through the maze of aisles packed with pop beads and earring backs and neon-hued paint. (I was not going to craft stores before I started doing burlesque.) I purchased three large plastic tubes in gold,

silver, and bronze. The sharp kind that, like burlesque dancers, can scratch, can cut when handled too rough.

52. I funneled these into a silver flask from Target that my friend Lady Ali Mode attached jewels to, screwed on the top, and shook up the flask before attaching it to my headband, which Ali also fashioned.

53. Glitter, glitter everywhere. I did this number for almost four years, not just in subsequent *Buttcrackers* but all over town at whatever bar would have me—since the act was my own, I could book it as much as I liked. People LOVED the glitter vodka act and since the color scheme wasn't red and green and the music was Duke Ellington, it could play year-round.

54. LUSH body bar and Martha Stewart craft glitter sticking on bare, pastie-d breasts.

55. It's a good thing.

56. Not a good thing: getting glitter *off* my bare, pastie-d breasts, torso, and neck after every performance, in time to get up in the morning and dress as an administrative assistant who was definitely *not* stripping the night before.

57. What no one told me about glitter is how fucking annoying it is to remove.

58. My friend Slightly Spitfire swears by a dry loofah. Not a wet one, that'll just spread sparkle around and if you're using craft glitter, will hurt you in the process.

59. A bone dry loofah basically sloughs the glitter off the skin, leaving red rub marks in its wake until it's time to slather on sparkle all over again. Hurts so good.

60. This does not, however, work for the glitter inevitably spilled or more often shed on bathroom tile, lead paint on furnaces in old apartment buildings, and pets.

61. There were Saturday mornings after a long night of shows when I'd find it on my cat: little sprinkles of silver on her

sleek black fur. Maybe a miniature gold star or two in the white of her tuxedo markings. I've no doubt the inadvertent application pissed her off.

62. Versace the cat is long gone now, but I still wonder if she was a burlesque dancer herself, in a previous life. You don't want glitter on you, unless you put it on yourself. Or you ask another to do it for you.

63. What no one told me about glitter is all the places it can go, especially when all those places are visible to the human eye.

64. Glitter also inevitably travels to the places you don't want it to go.

65. I've peed glitter multiple times. Once at a Starbucks before a Friday morning meeting.

66. What no one told me about glitter: it never fully leaves you.

67. Here's where I get all symbolic. I don't do burlesque much anymore, haven't since pre-pandemic 2020, for a bunch of different reasons I'm not going into here. But when I think about the years I spent under the hot spotlight, shivering in a barroom backroom, or hugging my fellow dancers—thus creating a sparkling mashup of whatever we were sporting that evening—I think about glitter.

68. I started my glitter journey with an atomizer of powder, soft and dreamy and barely-there, and ended with Martha Stewart, shiny and sharp, and can't-miss. Even with my burlesque career largely in the rearview mirror, I think about glitter: acquiring, applying, and removing, while acknowledging that in some ways, it's always here to stay.

69. Little did I know how much it would stick.

ABOUT THE CONTRIBUTORS

❖ Abby McKee is a sophomore at Ohio Northern University. She is currently studying pharmacy with minors in chemistry and communications. In her free time she enjoys reading and writing.

❖ Amanda Bennett is a queer Black Southern poet and educator living in Durham, North Carolina. She is the author of a dissertation centering practices of Black femme magic within Black women's literary history. As a graduate student, she collaborated with her students to found the poetry workshop series "Poetry as Pedagogy: Finding Healing and Community Through Writing." Previously, Amanda has published her short fiction and poetry in *Obsidian*, *Triangle Poets Series*, *The Concern Reading Series*, *Murder Journal,* and *Jellyfish Magazine*. She is also the founder of the Black feminist consulting and education collective, define&empower

❖ Amanda Brown is a digital copywriter moonlighting as a poet in St. Louis. Amanda's work has been published most recently in *Flowers Grow in Graveyards, Too* by Sunday Mornings at the River and Querencia Press's *Summer 2022 Anthology*.

❖ Anastasia Helena Fenald (b. 1992) is a second-generation Ukrainian-Hispanic-American poet from Los Angeles and the Mojave Desert. Known for her energetic attitude and sad poems, she spends most of her free time attending poetry workshops, performing at local open mics, and exploring Southern California. She has been published in the *Shelia-Na-Gig Online Journal, The Sims Library of Poetry's Anthology Poems in Praise of Libraries,* and *A Thousand Flowers Anthology* and more. Help Me, I'm Here: Poems to Myself (2022) is her debut poetry collection by the World Stage Press. Instagram: @anastasiafenald

❖ Andrew Daugherty (he/him) is a poet & novelist from Baltimore. He's the author of several unpublished works, including the pro wrestling roller derby noir *The Big Heel* and the poetry chapbook *Under the Weather Girls*. Past & upcoming homes for his work include COLORS: The Magazine and Bullshit Lit.

twitter: @andrew__3000
instagram: @andrew3stax

❖ Ann Kammerer (she/her) lives in Oak Park, Illinois, where she is a semi-retired copy and feature writer for small business and higher education. Her short fiction and poetry have appeared in several publications and on-line platforms, including *The Thoughtful Dog, Open Arts Forum, The Ekphrastic*

Review, and *Querencia Press.* She received top honors in fiction writing contests run by the Chicago-based Crow Woods Publishing and Toledo/Ann Arbor's *Current Magazine,* and made the top 10 in the 2018 Tillie Olsen Short Fiction Award sponsored by *The Tishman Review.* Ann's fiction was featured in the 2015 and 2020 anthologies of art-inspired short stories, *Visions of Life* and *Visions of Life 2,* produced by Crow Woods Publishing.

❖ Audrey Timmins, 21, is a writer located in St. Petersburg, Florida. Her pronouns are she/her/hers. Audrey writes short fiction and poetry, as well as studies law at Stetson University College of Law. She has published an ecological dystopian horror short story in the University of North Florida's journal the *Talon Review.* She currently works as a law clerk in Tampa, FL, and hopes to merge her love for law with her love for writing about American socio-political issues. When not in school, she can be found in Brooklyn, NY, with her partner and their cat, Princess.

❖ Recent work by Bruce Robinson appears or is forthcoming in *Tar River Poetry, Spoon River, Rattle, Mantis, Two Hawks Quarterly, Berkeley Poetry Review, Tipton Poetry Journal, North Dakota Quarterly, Last Stanza,* and *Aji.* He has raced whippets in the midwest and is part of that stubborn undercurrent in Brooklyn that continues to root for the Brooklyn Dodgers.

❖ Carella is a three-time offender with Querencia Press, published in Not Ghosts But Spirits, the quarterly anthology, and Scavengers. Her art and writing have appeared in numerous publications, including the cover of Glassworks 26, Columbia Journal, Skyie Magazine, Stripes Literary Magazine, Door is a Jar, Grub Street, Troublemaker Firestarter, Free Verse Revolution and Sunday Mornings at the River.

instagram.com/catalogue.of.dreams
twitter.com/catalogofdream

❖ Cathleen Balid is a student from Queens, New York. She edits for HaluHalo Journal and the Culinary Origami Review. In her free time, she loves to journal and go on sunset drives.

❖ Charlotte Ella Rosenblum is from San Francisco, California where she is currently a senior in highschool. She is an upcoming freshman at New York University studying abroad in London so that she can drink copious amounts of tea and stand in places where Virginia Woolf once stood. She has studied spoken word poetry at Interlochen Center for the Arts and was a finalist in the California Speech Association's original prose and poetry event.

❖ Christian Ward is a UK-based writer who has recently appeared in *The Dewdrop, Dodging the Rain, Blue Unicorn, The Seventh Quarry, Bluepepper, Tipton Poetry Journal, The Amazine* and *Rye Whiskey Review.*

- Dani De Luca is a teacher and writer. She holds a BA in Portuguese Language and an MA in TESOL. She resides outside Nashville with her husband and son. Find her work on Instagram @danidelucawriter.

- Daniel Moreschi is a poet from Neath, South Wales, UK. After life was turned upside down by his ongoing battle with severe M.E., he rediscovered his passion for poetry that had been dormant since his teenage years. Writing has served as a distraction from his struggles ever since. Daniel has been acclaimed by many poetry competitions, including the annual ones hosted by the Oliver Goldsmith Literature Festival, Wine Country Writers Festival, Short Stories Unlimited, Michigan Poetry Society, Westmoreland Arts & Heritage Festival, and Inchicore Ledwidge Society. Daniel has also had poetry published by Black Cat Poetry Press, and the The Society of Classical Poets.

- david diaz is a teacher and writer living in Los Angeles. In the past, his poetry has been published by The San Pedro River Review, Silver Birch Press, and he has appeared in an anthology by Tia Chucha Press. While completing his MFA at CSULB, david published two chapbooks with Tiny Splendor Press and is currently working on a new collection as he rediscovers being human.

- D.M. Rice is a non-binary writer from Dallas, TX, living abroad in England, having recently earned a PhD from the University of Essex, following a course in the Avant Gardes. They are editor of the literary journal, Sybil, and publish widely online and in print.

- Elaine Westnott-O'Brien is a writer and teacher of English language and literature. She writes in all forms, and her work has appeared in *The New York Times, The Wild Word* and *Forget Me Not Press*. She has work forthcoming in several journals, including *Papeachu Review* and *The Uncoiled*. She lives with her wife and two children in Tramore, Ireland. Find her on Instagram @elainewob_words.

- Eliza Marley is a graduate of Loyola University Chicago creative writing and film programs and is a current graduate student at University of Illinois Chicago program for writers. Eliza writes with magical realist and surrealist influences. A Queer and neurodivergent writer, much of her work looks at the mysteries hidden within the mundane, peeling back the trivialities of daily life to reveal something new and strange. In her spare time Eliza plays the harp and is an avid reader of folklore and mysteries. Eliza enjoys hiking, kayaking, and baking. She can often be found with a cup of tea and her cat, Theo, laying on top of whichever book she is trying to read.

- Elyssa Tappero (she/her) is radically queer, vocally pagan, and writes a lot of weird shit she hopes will leave you feeling vaguely disturbed. She enjoys alliteration, run-on sentences, killing characters, and making obscure references to historical events. You can find her work at onlyfragments.com and on Twitter at @OnlyFragments.

❖ Emily Levang (she/her) is an essayist living at the headwaters of Lake Superior, where her work envisions humans caring for our Earth-body. She is the Communications Manager for Waankam: People for the Estuary, a citizen-led Rights of Nature initiative. She has been published in Ensia, Earth Island Journal, MN Women's Press, MinnPost, Art Speaks Water, and the Social Fabric Zine. She is a graduate of the Stonecoast MFA in Maine.

❖ Emily Manzer is an emerging writer from Vancouver, BC.

❖ Francesca Leader is a self-taught writer and artist originally from Western Montana. Her writing has appeared or is forthcoming in Wigleaf, Fictive Dream, Barren, CutBank, Leon Literary, Apex Magazine, Anti-Heroin Chic, JMWW, and elsewhere. Learn more about her work at inabucketthemoon.wordpress.com

❖ Georgie Morvis (they/them) is a writer based in Chicago, by way of Kalaheo, Hawai'i and Las Cruces, New Mexico. Their writing is forthcoming from *Cast of Wonders*. They won the Judges' Prize for their short film script *Shrimp Heads* at the 'Ohina Filmmakers Lab 2022. They also were one of 10 finalists for the Dream Foundry Emerging Writers Contest 2022. When not writing, they enjoy reading, listening to Carly Rae Jepsen, and watching Greta Gerwig movies. You can follow them on Twitter at @gmorvis.

❖ Glendalee Diaz is a Dominican-American born and raised in New York. She self-published a book of poems and prose titled Café con Leche: Poems and Prose. Although writing is not her full-time occupation, she hopes to always be surrounded by stories.

❖ Hasrat is an author, poet, content creator, and entrepreneur who has been writing for five years now. She considers writing as an influential way of expression. Her conviction lies in illustrating love through her poetries. She is also a skilful litterateur. She believes that becoming the 2020 winner of the 9th Art Writer Essay Competition hosted by the University of Tsukuba, Japan, has set the stage right and created the ground for her ikigai. Hasrat also relishes spreading her intricate ideas through paintings, podcasts, and confabs. The Instagram page 'hapoetry.epoh' is her foundation. This keen and curious scholar lives in utopia and resides in the capital of India.

❖ Ixy is a Philadelphian poet that has been writing for about 15 years. During that time, she participated in a few local open mics and poetry slams. As of more recently she's looked more into the possibility of getting published as a means for even more people to hear her voice.

- Jacek Wilkos (he/him) is an engineer from Poland. He lives with his wife and two daughters in a beautiful city of Cracow. He is addicted to buying books, he loves black coffee, dark ambient music, and anything that's spooky. First he published his fiction in Polish online magazines, but in 2019 he started to translate his writing to English, and so far it was published in numerous anthologies by Black Hare Press, Black Ink Fiction, Alien Buddha Press, Eerie River Publishing, Insignia Stories, Reanimated Writers Press, Iron Faerie Publishing, KJK publishing, CultureCult, Wicked Shadow Press. You can find more about his writing at: https://www.facebook.com/Jacek.W.Wilkos/

- Jane Palmer (she/they) is a queer/non-binary professor, researcher, activist, and MFA student in Washington, DC. She writes poetry, creative non-fiction, picture books, and academic articles.. For the past 25 years, she has been dreaming of — and working toward — a world without violence. For the past 5 years, she and her child have been on a quest to find the best playground ever. Twitter: @jane_e_palmer.

- Janna Lopez is an intuitive book coach, creative writing teacher with an MFA, and published author. She uses intuition to guide individuals in transforming their lives through fearless writing, reimagining the power of poetry, and unlearning false beliefs about writing's purpose. Her next book, "The Art & Invitation of Self-Conversation—Writing That Moves You Beyond Fear to Freedom," is based on work with hundreds of clients. She leads writing retreats through Land of Enchantment Writing.

- Jess (she/her) is a musician-turned-writer and disability advocate from Australia. She lives with Ehlers-Danlos Syndrome, Fibromyalgia, Essential Tremor, and Pre-Menstrual Dysphoric Disorder. She is passionate about using her negative experiences in the healthcare field to help other members of the chronic illness and disability communities feel less alone, and empower them to practise fearless self-advocacy when necessary. You can see more of Jess' work on www.delicatelittlepetal.com or on Instagram @delicatelittlepages.

- Jo is an avid reader, inconsistent poet and regular cinemagoer currently living in Zürich, Switzerland. First poetry collection *Primary Poems* published in 2020.

- Karen Gonzalez-Videla (she/her/hers) is an Argentinian immigrant living in Florida. You can usually find her somewhere in nature, hiding among the animals and plants. Her writing has been featured in PANK, Menacing Hedge, Paranoid Tree, and other places. You can find her on Twitter at @Gv12Karen or on her website at https://kgonzalezvidela.carrd.co/.

- Kelly Cutchin (she/her/hers) should've been named YELLY and is a writer, teaching artist, and workshop facilitator based in suburban Colorado. She is the self-proclaimed DoorDash of downhome holler witches and a human interrobang. You can find her work Olney Magazine, Anti-Heroin Chic, and on pink Post-It Notes she sneaks into library books.

❖ Originally from Iowa, Kelsey Landhuis (she/her) is a queer writer currently living in Baltimore, Maryland with her partner and cats. She can be found on Instagram at @kelsey_landhuis

❖ Kristina Percy (she/her) lives on Vancouver Island, Canada in the traditional territories of the Ligwiłda'xw people. Neither of her degrees have anything to do with creative writing. Her work has been published extensively in her Gmail drafts folder.

❖ Lauren Emily Whalen (she/her) is a writer and performer living in Chicago with her black cat, Rosaline. Her fifth book, *Tomorrow and Tomorrow*, a female rock band reimagining of Shakespeare's *Macbeth* co-written with Lillah Lawson, will be released by Sword & Silk on October 17. Lauren is a regular contributor to Kirkus Reviews, GO Magazine, and Queerty/Q Digital. Learn more at laurenemilywrites.com.

❖ Leonie developed a passion for writing as a young girl on the island of Jamaica. Growing up beside her neighborhood library, Leonie would spend endless hours exploring the fascinating world that authors created through their compelling fictional works. This awakened her love for reading and writing. Her favorite genres are mystery and fantasy, but she prefers to write emotional poetry and realistic fiction. She migrated from the Caribbean, and now resides in the United States, where she teaches English Language Arts, and spend her days secretly trying to instill a of love of language and reading in her kids. Leonie is a published poet, relationship blogger, and nature enthusiast. She believes that poetry is able to "describe the indescribable, love the unlovable, feel the undeniable, and grieves with the inconsolable". She contends that this aforementioned quote is the principal reason she is impelled to write.

❖ Elizabeth Yew (She/They) writes under the nickname "Liz Yew" and has had poems published on multiple platforms since she began focusing on writing poetry. Liz grew up in Hong Kong and is now working on a BA in English literature and creative writing in the UK. She never understood poetry growing up, but since discovering Sylvia Plath's work, their own collection of (often depressing) reflective poetry quickly grew. Unfortunately, being away from home does mean missing her dogs, which they compensate for with her newfound hobby of crocheting.

❖ Lucas Kurmis is an MA Candidate in Writing and Literacy Studies at Northern Michigan University, a musician, and a multimedia artist. His art focuses on mental health, vulnerability, and the grays of fiction.

❖ Luis Lopez-Maldonado is a Xicanx activist, poeta, playwright, dancer, choreographer, and educator born and raised in Southern California. He/Him/They/Them earned a Bachelor of Arts degree from the University of California Riverside, in Creative Writing and Dance. His/Their poetry has been seen in *The American Poetry Review, Foglifter, The Packinghouse Review, Public Pool,* and *Latina Outsiders: Remaking Latina Identity,* among many others. He/They also earned a Master of Arts degree in Dance from Florida State University and a Master of Fine Arts degree in Creative Writing from the University of Notre Dame. He/They are currently adding glitter to the Land of Enchantment, working for the public educational system as a high school Bilingual Educator and Special Education Teacher, holding a Pre K-12 Special Education License and a Pre K-12 Specialty Area License, with endorsements in TESOL, Bilingual Education, Performing Arts, and English Language Arts. He/They are currently a candidate for the Education Specialist Certification and State Administration Licensure at the University of New Mexico.

❖ Luke Young (He/Him) is a writer, bibliophile, bartender, proletarian and factotum. He is of indigenous and European settler heritage. He grew up among Southeast Asian war refugees in the states of Washington and California before being moved to Cambodia at the age of five. He relocated back to the U.S. in 2017.

❖ M. Hutman is an outspoken Romani writer, free spirit and hopeful romantic. She is passionate about healing through creative outlets. She is an innovative soul who enjoys spending time in solitude: in the forest or near water. M. Hutman makes it a priority to be raw, vulnerable, unapologetic and to be doing the necessary work on her journey. When she's not writing poetry/prose she loves her daughter, art museums, botanical gardens, coffee and breaking the rules.

❖ Marshall Bood lives in Regina, Saskatchewan with his beautiful cat. His debut collection is *Spring Cleaning* (Ugly Duckling Presse, 2021).

❖ Milie is a millennial from the French Atlantic coast. She is currently teaching English as a foreign language in Bordeaux and adulting as best as she can. Having studied culture and linguistic, she wants her writing to push the envelope—and maybe even fold it into a quirky little paperplane. You can also find some of her work in Flare Journal, Dead Skunk Mag, The Literary Canteen, Penumbra Journal, orangepeel, Querencia's Autumn 2022 anthology, Defunct Mag, and soon Juste Milieu Zine.

❖ OLIVIA SNOWDROP is a queer non-binary poet from Manchester, UK. They are the author of two self-published poetry books: *Snowdrop,* and their latest collection, *ANTS IN A JAM JAR.* Olivia is also active on Instagram as @oliviasnowdrop (when such activity isn't detrimental to her mental health!) and has been previously published in *Honeyfire Literary Magazine, Pulp Poets Press, orangepeel literary magazine, Free Verse Revolution,* and *fifth wheel press.*

- Sam Indigo Lydia Sword Fern Parker (they/theirs/she/hers) is a queer nonbinary trans woman, 26 years old, and a Taurus Rising. They are a white settler on occupied Wintu ancestral and current territory, colonially named Redding, California. She is an enthusiast of planets and plants, and they hope to encourage heightened awareness and engagement with the many systems we inhabit and propel in our daily lives.

- Sara Doty received her Master of Fine Arts in creative writing from Stetson University in 2022. She is a United States Marine Corps veteran. She writes fiction and poetry.

- Sari Richards (they/them) is a queer writer based in upstate New York. In Spring 2022, Sari graduated from Binghamton University, with a bachelor's degree in English and a master's degree in Sustainable Communities. They have been writing consistently from a young age and continued developing skills as a writer and reader throughout college and graduate school. Sari's writing, historically and presently, has drawn from the following experiences: growing up trans and queer; substance use issues, addiction, and recovery; mental illness/madness; chronic illness; neuro-divergence. They are particularly drawn to the concepts of boundaries, memory, language, sound, relations, and visibility.

- Steve Denehan lives in Kildare, Ireland with his wife Eimear and daughter Robin. He is the author of two chapbooks and four poetry collections. Winner of the Anthony Cronin Poetry Award and twice winner of Irish Times' New Irish Writing, his numerous publication credits include Poetry Ireland Review and Westerly.

- A former Pulitzer finalist and winner of the Poets' Prize, Sydney Lea served as founding editor of *New England Review* and was Vermont's Poet Laureate from 2011 to 2015. He is the author of twenty-three books: a novel, five volumes of personal and three of critical essays, and fourteen poetry collections, most recently *Here* (Four Way Books, NYC, 2019). A fifteenth book of poems, *What Shines,* is due in September, 2023. In 2021, he was presented with his home state of Vermont's most prestigious artist's distinction: the Governor's Award for Excellence in the Arts.

- Zoe Copeland is a writer from the Westcountry (UK), inspired by their lived experiences and drawn to the description of micro-experiences. They are motivated to incorporate their experiences of being queer, neurodivergent, and of the marginalization they have faced, and equally to share their enlightening experiences of spiritual moments - often in nature. Through their writing, Zoe hopes to connect to others with similar experiences, illuminate taboo subjects, and evoke contemplation.

OTHER TITLES FROM QUERENCIA

CPSIA information can be obtained
at www.ICGtesting.com
Printed in the USA
BVHW050415260423
663005BV00015B/855

9 781959 118503